333.72 Kid.

£9.99

MANAGING

COSYSTEMS

Adrian Kidd

Hodder & Stoughton

A MEMBER OF THE HODDER HEADLINE GROUP

Acknowledgements

The publishers would like to thank the following for giving permission to reproduce copyright photographs in this book: Figure 1.5.2, Environmental Images; Figure 1.5.3, Figure 3.1.7, Figure 3.2.14, Figure 4.1.7, Figure 4.2.6, Figure 4.5.3, Figure 5.4.6, Figure 5.5.11, Figure 5.6.7, Life File; Figure 4.3.6, Figure 4.4.3, Figure 5.6.2, Corbis; Figure 5.6.10, The Environment Agency. All other photographs provided by the author.

Every effort has been made to contact the holders of copyright material used in this book, but if any have been overlooked, the publishers will be pleased to make the necessary alterations at the first opportunity.

Orders: please contact Bookpoint Ltd, 39 Milton Park, Abingdon, Oxon OX14 4TD. Telephone: (44) 01235 400414, Fax: (44) 01235 400454. Lines are open from 9.00–6.00, Monday to Saturday, with a 24 hour message answering service. Email address: orders@bookpoint.co.uk

British Library Cataloguing in Publication Data
A catalogue record for this title is available from The British Library

ISBN 0 340 72495 1

First published 1999
Impression number   10 9 8 7 6 5 4 3 2 1
Year   2004 2003 2002 2001 2000 1999

Cover photo by Science Photo Library
Typeset by Fakenham Photosetting Limited, Fakenham Norfolk NR21 8NL
Printed in China for Hodder & Stoughton Educational, a division of Hodder Headline Plc, 338 Euston Road, London NW1 3BH by Sun Fung Offset Binding Co., Ltd.

Contents

INTRODUCTION

Ecology is becoming an increasingly important component in all Advanced level Geography syllabuses, and reflects growing concern among both geographers, and the general public about the implications of human activities on the natural environment.

In both the UK and the USA the conservation of both nature and landscapes, has a long history. In the UK, the Sea Birds Protection Act and the Wild Birds Protection Act date back to 1869 and 1880 respectively. The Royal Society for the Protection of Birds was founded in 1889, the National Trust in 1894, and the British Ecological Society in 1913. In the USA, the world's first national park, the Yellowstone, was established in 1872.

The need, in the UK, for the protection of specific areas of countryside was prompted by increasing concern, especially between 1918 and 1939, over the loss of agricultural land to urbanisation, the loss of public access to 'open' spaces, and the loss of natural habitats, particularly in the uplands, to agricultural 'improvement' and afforestation.

The 'modern' environmental or ecological movement began in the 1960s when concern about the damage to the environment, through human activities, began to make national and international news. In 1962, a graphic account of the effect on wildlife of pesticides such as DDT, and other man made chemicals, was provided with the publication by Rachel Carson of 'Silent Spring'. The effects of atmospheric nuclear tests, which led to the growth of the Campaign for Nuclear Disarmament, and vivid television images of oil tanker disasters, such as the *Torrey Canyon* in 1967, and the *Amoco Cadiz* 1978, all added to the public's awareness of environmental problems.

The year 1970 proved to be very significant in environmental terms, with the founding of both Greenpeace and Friends of the Earth. It was also European Conservation Year, and the year in which the Environmental Protection Agency was established in the USA, and the Department of the Environment in the UK.

In 1972, the 'Limits to Growth', was published by the Club of Rome. It examined world trends in agricultural production, natural resources, industrial production, and population, and concluded, because of a resource crisis, that the earth system would collapse before 2100. Further reports, including the 'World Conservation Strategy' in 1980, the Brandt Report on 'North and South: a Programme for Survival and Common Crisis' in 1983, and the Brundtland Report 'Our Common Future' in 1987, all stressed the need for a change in attitude to the use of natural resources. The Brundtland Report was the first to stress the concept of sustainable development, and defined it as 'development that meets the needs of the present without compromising the ability of future generations to meet their own needs'. In Europe in the 1970s and 1980s, the environmental movement became a political force with the growth of the Green Party or Die Grunen, which was particularly successful in West Germany. In Britain, the Green Party, achieved its best result in the 1989 election, but never quite achieved the success of Die Grunen.

The 1980s and 1990s have seen growing concern over many environmental issues including acid rain, the destruction of the ozone layer, global warming, endangered species, and the loss of habitats. All of these issues have been discussed at international conferences, many of which have resulted in legislation to protect the environment.

The purpose of this book is to investigate how the earth's ecosystems are being affected by human activities, and to consider how they may be successfully managed. Chapters 1 and 2 provide an introduction to the basic principles of ecology. The impact of human activities, on the major global ecosystems (biomes), is outlined in Chapters 3 and 4, and on the major ecosystems of the British Isles in Chapter 5. The book concludes with Chapter 6 providing a review of international, national and local strategies for the management of ecosystems.

Apart from the references given at the end of the book much useful up-to-date information may be obtained from:
- the 'BBC Wildlife' magazine, and its web site at www.bbc.co.uk/animalzone/wildmag.shtml, and
- the various regular magazines including 'English Nature', 'Site Lines', 'Urban wildlife News', and 'Nature's Place' published by English Nature, and its web site at www.english-nature.org.uk.

STUDENT ACTIVITY

The *Sunday Times Magazine* of 26 February 1989 was a special edition devoted to environmental problems. Its front cover carried the headline:
**'The world is dying -
what are you going to do about it?'**
1 Why do you think the newspaper felt that such a special edition was needed at that time?
2 To what extent do you agree with the first part of the headline?
3 Outline how you can help to minimise your impact on the environment.

1
THE NATURE OF
ECOSYSTEMS

Key Ideas

■ Ecosystems consist of living organisms and their material environments of soil, air and water, and occur at a variety of scales.

■ Energy from the sun is converted by the producers into living material. Some energy is lost at each trophic level as it flows through the ecosystem.

■ Nutrients are recycled between the biomass, the leaf litter, the soil, and nutrient stores in the atmosphere, the hydrosphere and the lithosphere.

■ As a result of a variety of processes mature soils have distinctive horizons.

■ People are an increasingly important component in ecosystems, due to increasing numbers, adaptability and technological expertise.

■ Agricultural activity is particularly significant in altering the functioning and structure of natural ecosystems.

■ Soils are the result of the interaction of parent material, climate, vegetation, relief and time.

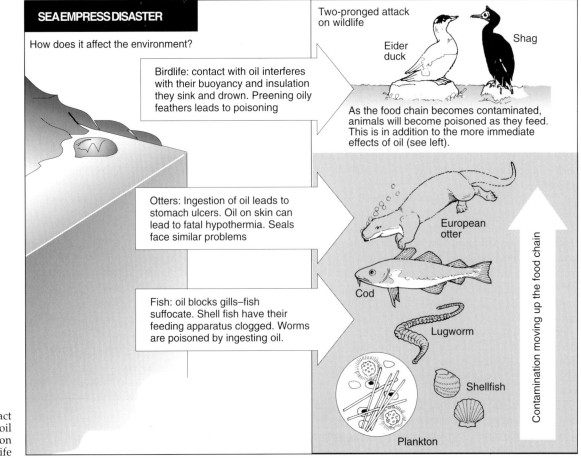

FIGURE 1.0.1 The impact of the *Sea Empress* oil pollution incident on wildlife

A combination of human population increase, economic development, and advances in technology are subjecting the natural environment to a series of threats. Recent pollution incidents, such as the 1993 Braer, and 1996 Sea Empress oil spills (Figure 1.0.1), have indicated the need for a thorough knowledge of natural environmental systems, if the impact of such events is to be fully understood. **Ecology** is the science which investigates the relationships of living organisms to each other, and their surroundings. The term ecology was first used by Ernst Haeckel in 1869, and is derived from the Greek 'oikos' or 'living space', and 'logos' meaning the science of.

STUDENT ACTIVITY 1.1

Use Figure 1.0.1 to help you to explain how oil pollution affects wildlife.

The organisms living on the surface layer of the Earth form the **biosphere**, and are found in the air (*atmosphere*), on land (the *lithosphere*), and in water (the *hydrosphere*). At a global scale, land environments with similar plant and animal communities form 'natural regions' or **biomes**. Each biome may be divided, at a variety of scales, into ecological systems or **ecosystems**. Each ecosystem has a unique range of species forming its biological diversity or **biodiversity**.

As with all systems, the ecosystem is composed of a series of inputs, processes or stores, and outputs. Although various components within it may change, it is usually maintained in a state of balance, called *dynamic equilibrium*. This stability is due to *homeostatic mechanisms*, which work rather like the thermostat in a central heating system. In an ecosystem, changes may be shown by feedback, which is the ability of the output to control the input. Negative feedback tends to increase stability, whereas positive feedback tends to increase instability within the system.

A G Tansley defined an ecosystem as:

'a particular category of physical systems consisting of organisms and inorganic components in a relatively stable equilibrium, open and of various kinds and sizes'.

An alternative definition by I G Simmons is: 'a unit of space-time containing living organisms interacting with each other, and with their abiotic environment by the interchange of energy and materials'.

A definition used by an examination board is: 'ecosystems consist of structured webs or systems at a range of scales, which include living organisms and their material environments of soil, air and water. These components are linked by movements of energy and nutrients'.

Land based, or terrestrial ecosystems, reflect the interrelationships between six major factors, plants, animals, humans, soil conditions, geology or rock type, and climate.

The study of a single plant or animal species is termed *autecology*. *Synecology* is the study of plant or animal (biotic) communities, and the interactions between them, and their physical (abiotic) environment, or habitat. This approach forms the basis of biogeography, and is the one which will be followed throughout this text.

1.1 Human Activities and Ecosystems

Throughout the last twenty years, in many countries, there has been an increasing awareness of the impact that human activities (**anthropogenic**) are having on the natural environment. Newspapers, frequently, feature environmental issues such as global warming, deforestation, desertification, acid rain, and the effects of oil spills and other types of pollution as leading stories. This has been paralleled by a growth in the membership of environmental pressure groups (Figure 1.1.1), including Greenpeace, Friends of the Earth, WWF, the Royal Society for the Protection of Birds, and the Council for the Protection of Rural England (CPRE).

Organisation	Membership in thousands		
	1971	**1981**	**1990**
Council for the Protection of Rural England	21	29	44
Friends of the Earth	1	18	110
Greenpeace UK	–	30	372
National Trust	278	1046	2032
Royal Society for the Protection of Birds	98	441	844
World Wide Fund for Nature	12	60	247

FIGURE 1.1.1 The membership of environmental organisations

FIGURE 1.1.2 Types of human impact

Agriculture	Urbanisation	Industry
Increased pesticide and herbicide use	Loss of natural habitats	Loss of natural habitats
Irrigation and salinisation	Pollution from carbon dioxide, sulphur dioxide, and other gases	Pollution from carbon dioxide, sulphur dioxide, and other gases
Drainage of wetlands	Increased surface run-off and flood risk	Derelict land
Overgrazing and overcropping		Pollution from heavy metals
Increased fertiliser application	Change in local climate	Water pollution
Water pollution from nitrates and slurry	Global warming	Hazardous wastes e.g. nuclear
Domestication of plants and animals	Acid rain	Global warming
Tree and hedgerow loss	Destruction of the ozone layer	Acid rain
Soil erosion	Creation of semi-rural habitats e.g. gardens	Destruction of the ozone layer
Biotechnology	Landfill sites (domestic waste)	
Desertification		

Mining	Forestry	Water industry
Loss of natural habitats	Deforestation	River abstraction
Changes in drainage and surface run-off	Afforestation	Waste disposal
Soil erosion	Soil erosion	Building of reservoirs
Dumping of waste material		

Why has there been an increase in the impact of human activities? The two basic factors to consider are the increase in the world's population from 1 m, approximately 300 000 years ago, to 5840 million in 1997, and the increasing use of technology associated with economic development.

Three trends may be identified in relation to the degree of the impact of human activities:

1 The number of ways in which human activities may affect the environment is constantly increasing.
2 Initially local issues, for example pesticides, are now becoming global issues as pesticide residues are found in polar areas.
3 The complexity, magnitude, and frequency of the impacts are increasing.

The degree of the impact depends upon:

1 Predisposing factors – some types of ecosystems are more prone to 'stress'.
2 Inciting factors – these are the human factors, for example deforestation or drainage, that produce the 'stress'.
3 Contributing factors – these amplify the degree of 'stress', for example if drainage was to be carried out during the warmer summer months its effect would be increased.

Ecosystems respond in different ways to human impacts. Some including lake ecosystems are highly vulnerable to change. Three concepts may be used to describe the ability of an ecosystem to withstand change. Its *elasticity* is its ability to recover from damage, its *resilience* is the frequency that it can recover from the stress caused by a particular event, and its *inertia* is its ability to resist change. Estuarine ecosystems are particularly resilient to change having adapted to the twice daily tidal regime.

STUDENT ACTIVITY 1.2

1 Write a brief definition of the following terms; *ecology*, *biosphere*, *biome*, *ecosystem* and *anthropogenic*.
2 With reference to Figure 1.1.1, explain the growth in the membership of environmental organisations.
3 Imagine you are the publicity officer for one of the organisations, and prepare a suitable A4 advertisement for the organisation.

At a local scale, it is possible to classify natural ecosystems based on the degree of human interference:

1 Natural habitats: these have developed with no human interference.
2 Degraded habitats: areas which are occasionally affected by, for example, forestry or grazing.
3 Ruderal habitats: here disturbance is regular, but there is no deliberate introduction of new species, for example, road side verges.
4 Cultivated habitats: these habitats are constantly disturbed and are dominated by introduced species.
5 Artificial habitats: these may be almost totally altered in terms of both species and environment, for example, large urban areas.

STUDENT ACTIVITY 1.3

1 Summarise the main ways in which human activities can modify ecosystems.
2 Select one factor from each of the five boxes in Figure 1.1.3 and explain how it will be affected by a decrease in vegetation.

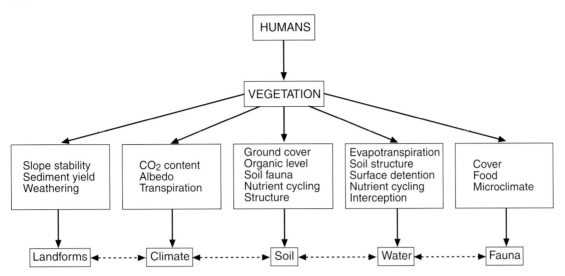

FIGURE 1.1.3 Some of the factors affected by human induced vegetation change

1.2 The Structure of Ecosystems

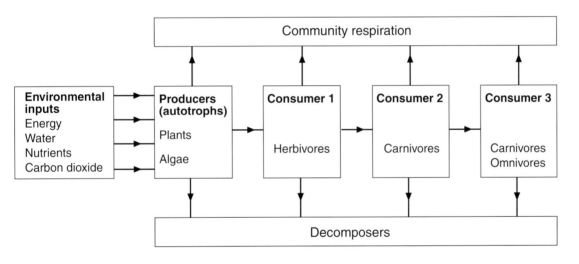

FIGURE 1.2.1 A model of the structure of an ecosystem

The term 'structure' refers to the various components which combine to produce an ecosystem. These may be divided into living or **biotic** components, and non-living or **abiotic** components.

The biotic component – producers and consumers

The living organisms in an ecosystem collectively form its **community** or population. Each organism interacts with others forming relatively simple **food chains** and complex **food webs**. Energy and nutrients pass through the ecosystem, as various organisms are in turn eaten by other organisms. Each stage in the food chain is called a **trophic level** (*trophos* = feeding). The primary producers or **autotrophs** form the first trophic level (Figure 1.2.1). These are mainly green plants, but the term also includes blue-green algae, and green and purple sulphur bacteria, all of which can carry out

> ### STUDENT ACTIVITY 1.4
>
> **1** Define each of the following terms: *biotic, trophic level, autotrophs, heterotrophs, herbivores, carnivores, omnivores, decomposers.*
> **2** Draw a simple diagram to outline the main features of the structure of an ecosystem.

photosynthesis. In marine and lake aquatic ecosystems, algae or **phytoplankton**, are usually dominant.

Primary producers form the food for the consumers or **heterotrophs** (*heteros* = other). Primary consumers, or **herbivores**, form the second trophic level, feeding directly on the producers. In land based ecosystems they will include grazing and browsing animals such as antelope and giraffe, together with plant eating insects and birds. In aquatic ecosystems, molluscs such as mussels, and **zooplankton** (small crustaceans and protozoa) which feed on **phytoplankton**, are the main primary consumers. The third trophic level comprises the secondary consumers or **carnivores**, which feed on the herbivores. A fourth trophic level, the tertiary consumers, who are also carnivores may occur. Some of the higher level consumers, for example bears, eat both plants and animals, and are called **omnivores**. There are several different groups of secondary and tertiary consumers:

1 *Predators* are those, which hunt, capture and kill their prey.
2 *Carrion feeders* consume dead and dying animals.
3 *Parasites* live on their host animal.

The **decomposers** and **detrivores** form another major component of the biotic structure of an ecosystem. After plants and animals die, they and their waste products are decomposed by *saprophytic* micro – organisms such as fungi and bacteria. Very small decomposing fragments form *detritus*, which is then fed on by small animals, detrivores, including earthworms and woodlice.

STUDENT ACTIVITY 1.5

Use Figure 1.2.2 to produce a table classifying the organisms into Producers, Primary Consumers, Secondary Consumers, etc.

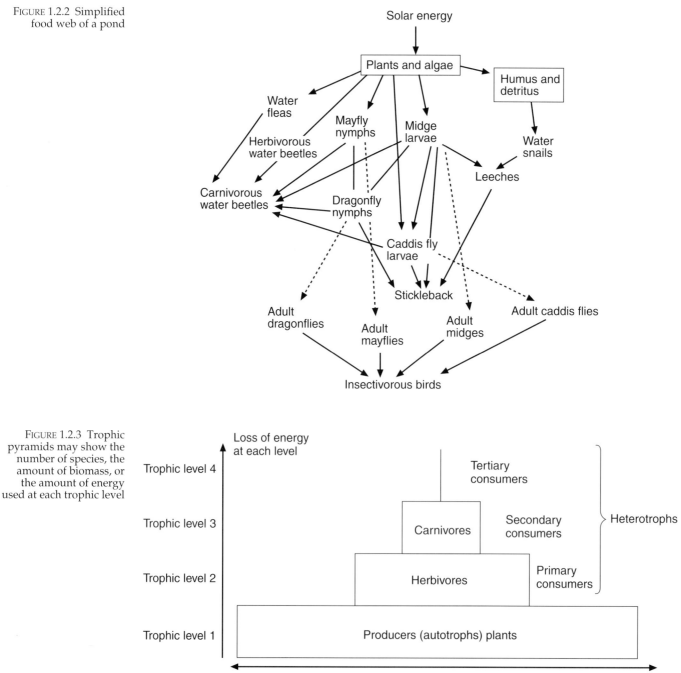

FIGURE 1.2.2 Simplified food web of a pond

FIGURE 1.2.3 Trophic pyramids may show the number of species, the amount of biomass, or the amount of energy used at each trophic level

The abiotic component – microclimate and soils

The environmental conditions associated with a particular plant or animal community form its **habitat**. Each habitat has unique biotic and environmental characteristics. The two dominant abiotic components are the habitat's microclimate and soil conditions. In the laboratory, under single species conditions, it is possible to identify the *physiological optimum* conditions for a particular species. They are, however, rarely identical to the *ecological optimum* conditions for a plant species, in a natural ecosystem, forming part of a plant community. Each organism can survive under a range of conditions (Figure 1.2.4). Organisms, such as the grass sheep's fescue, which can tolerate a wide range of conditions, are *eurytopic*, whereas *stenotopic* species, such as wavy hair grass, can only survive in a limited range of conditions.

Microclimate conditions

The climate of an area is the result of the interplay between latitude, relief, aspect, the influence of the sea, and the effect of different air masses. Specific aspects of the climate of an area are obviously important to the growth of a particular plant species, and combine to produce the micro or local climate of the habitat:

1 *Temperature* Temperatures determine the rates of biochemical reactions in plants, with the reactions approximately doubling with every 10°C increase. Each plant species has a minimum temperature below which it is inactive, and a maximum temperature above which biochemical reactions cease. Growth in many plants will occur when temperatures are above 6°C. The number of days above this figure is then the length of the growing season. Plants in areas with extremes of temperature, such as the tundra and tropical deserts, have mechanisms which allow them to adapt to such conditions.

2 *Light levels* In order to allow it to carry out photosynthesis, each plant has its own light requirements, related to light intensity, light duration (photoperiod) and light quality (wavelength). Most plants can tolerate a range of light intensity, but some plants, termed *heliophytes*, require high levels, whereas *sciophytes* can grow in shady, low light conditions. In a typical, forest plant community the tallest trees, with the highest light demands, form the *euphotic* layer below which is the *oligophotic* layer. The *mesophotic* layer is formed by trees which are adapted to average light levels. Plants and shrubs, which grow in shade, at ground level form the *dysphotic* layer.

3 *Water requirements* Water is essential for a variety of biochemical plant processes, including photosynthesis. Land plants obtain approximately 98 per cent of their water requirements, by water passing from the soil into plant roots, by the process

of osmosis. The water then passes through the plant and, any which has not been used in biochemical processes, is transpired through the leaf stomata. Plants vary in their water requirements. *Hydrophytes* grow in fresh water and are unable to tolerate drought. *Xerophytes* are adapted to survive long periods of drought, and *halophytes* are able to survive in saline water. *Mesophytes* cannot survive in waterlogged soils or through a longer period of drought, they require 'average' conditions and are the typical plants of temperate areas.

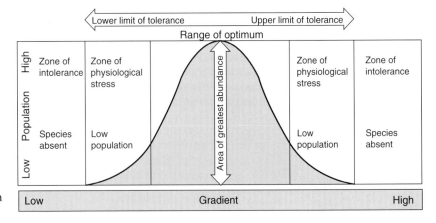

FIGURE 1.2.4 The frequency of an organism along the gradient of a physical factor in its environment

---

STUDENT ACTIVITY 1.6

Produce a table to describe the average temperatures and precipitation for each of the biomes indicated on Figure 1.2.5.

FIGURE 1.2.5 Distribution of major biomes in relation to average annual precipitation and average annual temperature

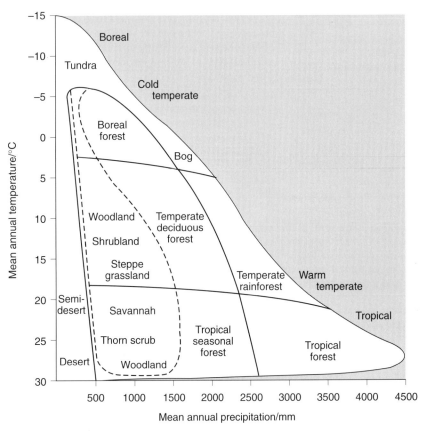

Soil (edaphic) conditions

In most land ecosystems the soil is the major store of nutrients, and moisture, available to plants. When a rock is weathered, it is broken down into a collection of different inorganic or mineral particles, including sand and clay, collectively known as the **regolith**. Organic material, resulting from the decomposition of plant and animal material called **humus**, may then be incorporated into the regolith to produce a soil. Soil also includes water, air and a variety of soil organisms or biota. Soil is the result of the interaction between climate, parent rock, plant and animal organisms (biota), topography (relief) and time. H Jenny, in 1941, represented these factors, in the following formula:

s = f(cl, o, r, p, t ...)

where *s* is a soil property, *cl* is the climate, *o* the biota, *r* the topography, *p* the parent rock, *t* is time and the dots represent other possible factors.

The climate is important as it influences the type, and rate of the weathering of the parent rock. Weathering is most intense in humid tropical areas where conditions permit extensive chemical weathering and at its lowest in the dry conditions of tropical arid areas. Climate also influences the nature of the vegetation, which will grow on a particular soil surface. Plants and animals recycle nutrients through growth, death and decomposition, and produce the humus material essential to soil fertility. Relief or topography affects climate and water movement. Steep slopes will lose or shed water, which will then move down slope to flatter receiving slopes. As the water moves, nutrients and soil particles also move down slope to be deposited at the base of the slope. This process often results in a particular sequence of soils, called a **soil catena**, developing on a parent rock along the slope profile.

FIGURE 1.2.6 The soil system

Rock types vary enormously in their resistance to weathering. A rock such as metaquarzite, which is almost entirely composed of quartz (silicon dioxide), is both very resistant to weathering and of poor nutrient status. The nature of the rock type will influence the colour of the soil, its texture, depth and drainage characteristics. For a 'mature' soil to develop, time is essential. It is necessary to allow time for the weathering processes to break down a rock, to produce the regolith, and for plants and animals to produce organic matter, which can then be incorporated into the regolith to form a soil. The soil can be viewed as a system with a variety of inputs, processes and outputs (Figure 1.2.6):

Soil Mineral Matter

The mineral matter found in soils is derived from the weathering of rock material, and consists of two types:
■ Primary unaltered minerals such as quartz.
■ Secondary minerals produced as a consequence of the weathering of primary minerals. These include several types of clays, and iron and aluminium oxides (sesquioxides).

Soil Texture

Soil is composed of a range of different sized mineral particles, varying from clay to gravel. The varying percentages, of each type of particle, produce soils with different characteristics. Sandy soils usually drain freely, but this factor means that they often have very low levels of moisture available to plants and are quickly leached of soil nutrients. Clay soils, however, are poorly drained but are less easily leached. Consequently, a soil termed a loam, containing both sand and clay particles, is preferable.

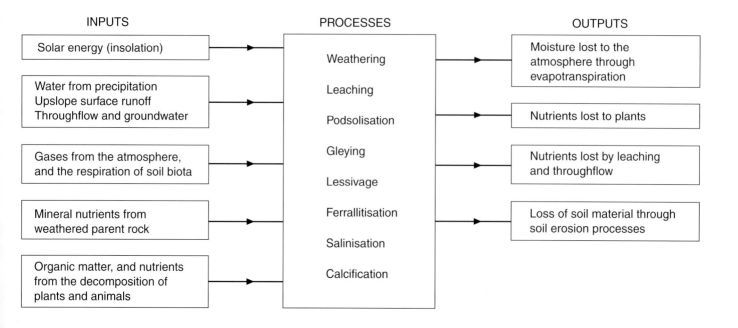

STUDENT ACTIVITY 1.7

1 Refer to Figure 1.2.7 and calculate the percentages of sand, silt and clay for soil types A, B and C.
2 What is the difference between soil texture and soil structure?
3 How does the texture and structure of a soil affect its management?

FIGURE 1.2.8
Classification of soil
particle size

Texture Class	Particle Size (mm)
Coarse sand	1.0–0.2
Fine sand	0.2–0.02
Silt	0.02–0.002
Clay	less than 0.002

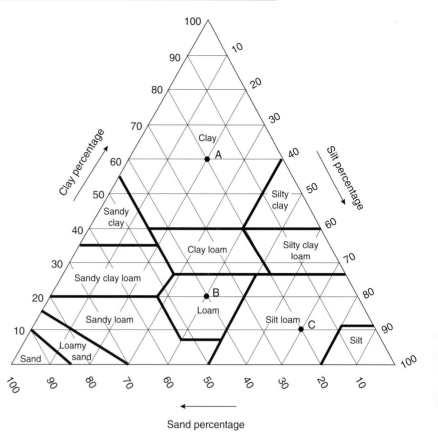

FIGURE 1.2.7 A triangular graph illustrating soil texture classes

Soil Structure and Soil Moisture

Soil particles aggregate together to form different structural shapes called *peds*. These structures may be classified into *crumb, granular, platy, blocky, prismatic* and *columnar*, and are important in determining the soil fabric or percentage of pore space available for moisture and air in a particular soil. Particular sized pores have specific functions related to the movement of air and moisture in a soil:

■ *Macropores or gravitational pores* are those over 0.075 mm which permit the rapid movement of air and moisture. If these pores are full of water the soil is waterlogged, and eventually the surplus water will drain away.
■ *Mesopores or capillary pores* are those between 0.075 and 0.030 mm. These act as reservoirs of water for plants. When all these pores are full of water the soil has reached its *field capacity*.
■ *Micropores or hygroscopic pores* are less than 0.030 mm and contain water, which is unavailable to plants.

Soil Organic Matter

The material called humus is formed by the decomposition of plant and animal matter. The rate of decay depends upon the nature of the material and the climate. The highest rates of decomposition occur in tropical rain forests. If leaves and other plant material are still recognisable in the humus it forms leaf litter (L). After further decomposition this material will produce the fermentation or humification layer (F). Eventually humus (H) is produced and incorporated into the soil, producing clay-humus complexes, which are important stores of soil nutrients. Humus formed under acid conditions is known as *mor* humus. Intermediate pH levels produce a type called *moder*, and alkaline conditions result in *mull* humus.

Soil Organisms

The organisms in the soil are vital in carrying out three main groups of processes:

1 *Decomposition*
Organic material, such as leaf litter, is broken down by bacteria, fungi, actinomycetes, and earthworms. Bacteria and fungi are also able to breakdown soil mineral matter, releasing nutrients.

2 *Transformation and fixations*
Nitrogen is an essential plant nutrient and is obtained either from rain water or from nitrogen gas in the air. Soil bacteria such as *Azobacter* and symbiotic bacteria such as *Rhizobium* living in the root nodules of leguminous plants, including clover and alfalfa, are able to fix nitrogen from the air. Some types of bacteria are also able to transform pesticides and herbicides into less toxic compounds.

3 *Structural processes*
Actinomycetes and fungi help mineral particles to bind together forming larger structures (peds), and earthworms, insects and burrowing mammals, such as moles, assist in the development of soil pore spaces.

Soil Nutrients

Nutrients in the soil are derived from the weathering of rock material, nutrients in rain water, the fixing of gases by soil and plant bacteria and the decomposition of plant and animal matter. They are available to plants in several forms:

- in solution in soil water,
- attached to the clay-humus complex, or
- nutrients produced by the weathering of rock material.

The clay-humus complex is the most important source of nutrients. The nutrients are attached, or *adsorbed*, to the surface of the clay and humus, in the clay-humus complex, as a consequence of their electrical charge. The clay and humus surfaces have a negative electrical charge produced by negative ions (anions) but many of the mineral nutrients, including calcium (Ca^{++}), sodium (Na^+), potassium (K^+), and magnesium (Mg^{++}), have a positive charge (cations). This allows them to be adsorbed onto the clay or humus surface, producing a double layer of negative and positive charges called the Gouy Layer.

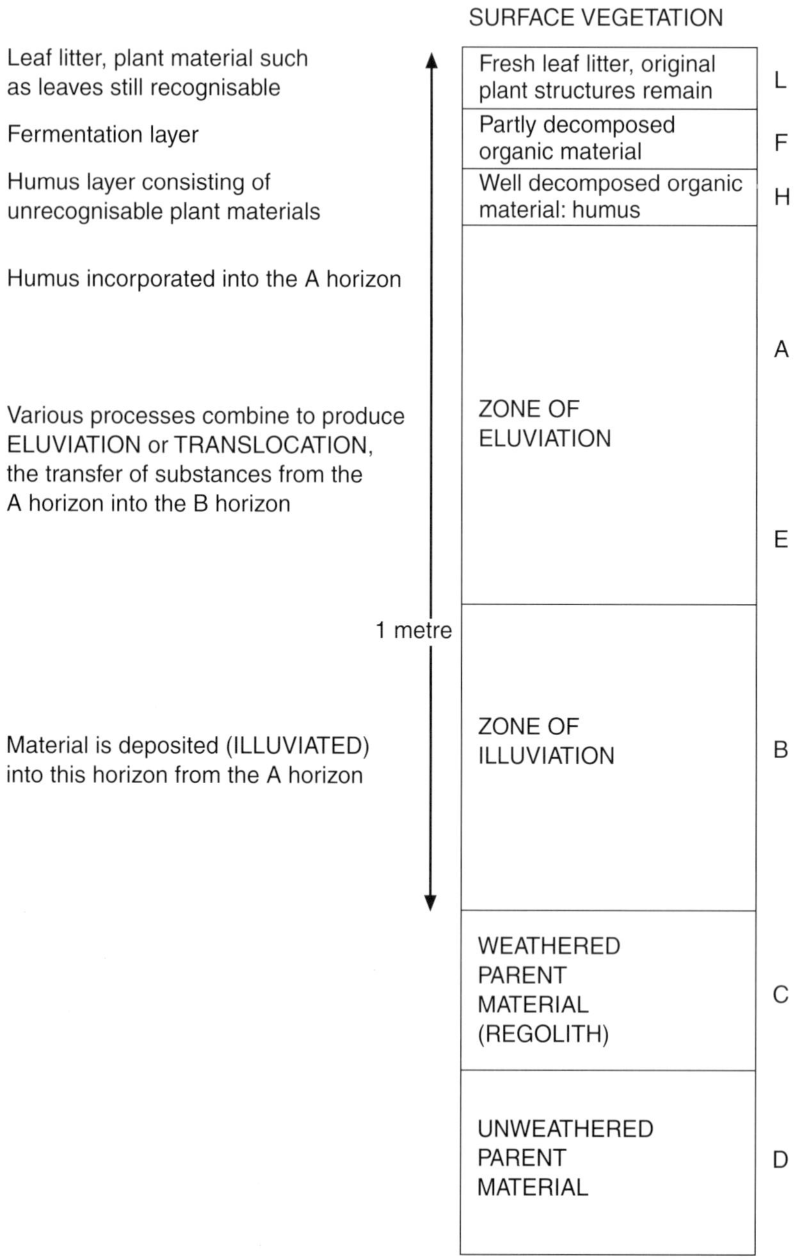

Plant rootlets also have a surface of negative ions, adsorbed onto which are positively charged hydrogen ($H+$) ions produced by the plant. The plant obtains nutrients by the process of *cation exchange*, where positively charged nutrients on the clay-humus complex are exchanged for positively charged hydrogen ions on the plant rootlet. The nutrients are then absorbed into the plant by osmosis. If this process continues, without nutrients such as calcium and potassium being replaced, the hydrogen concentration in the soil increases, reducing the pH level and producing acidic conditions. The ability of a soil to exchange cations is its *Cation Exchange Capacity (CEC)*, and is related to its humus content and the type of clay it contains.

Some plant nutrients, including nitrate (NO_{3-}), phosphate (PO_{4-}) and sulphate (SO_{4-}), are negatively charged (anions). This results in them being easily lost (leached) from the soil as they are unable to be absorbed onto the surface of the clay-humus complex.

Figure 1.2.9 Theoretical soil profile (where precipitation exceeds evapotranspiration)

SURFACE VEGETATION

Leaf litter, plant material such as leaves still recognisable

Fermentation layer

Humus layer consisting of unrecognisable plant materials

Humus incorporated into the A horizon

Various processes combine to produce ELUVIATION or TRANSLOCATION, the transfer of substances from the A horizon into the B horizon

1 metre

Material is deposited (ILLUVIATED) into this horizon from the A horizon

Fresh leaf litter, original plant structures remain	L
Partly decomposed organic material	F
Well decomposed organic material: humus	H
ZONE OF ELUVIATION	A / E
ZONE OF ILLUVIATION	B
WEATHERED PARENT MATERIAL (REGOLITH)	C
UNWEATHERED PARENT MATERIAL	D

Soil pH

The level of concentration of hydrogen ions in the soil produces the pH of the soil. It is measured on a scale from 2 to 12, with 7 being *neutral*, values over 7 being *alkaline* and values below 7 being *acidic*. The pH of the soil is important in terms of nutrient availability and the level of soil biota activity, with both having optimum pH levels between approximately 5.5 and 7. At higher pH values, nutrients are often insoluble and unavailable to plants resulting in deficiencies of iron and phosphorus. At lower values, nutrients are very soluble and may be leached from the soil, producing a toxic soil with high levels of dissolved iron and aluminium. Plants, which tolerate low pH (acid) conditions, are termed **calcifuges** (lime-hating). Those which prefer high pH (basic) conditions are **calcicoles** (lime-loving).

Soil Horizons

If a vertical cut is made through a section of soil, a soil profile will be produced. In most soils it will be apparent that the soil consists of a series of layers, or **horizons**, produced by the movement of soil materials through the profile. A typical soil profile in an area where soil water, normally, moves downwards consists of four horizons (Figure 1.2.9).

Soil Forming Processes

Soils are the product of a large number of complex processes which include:
1 Weathering – the breaking down of rock material by physical, chemical and biotic processes.
2 Organic accumulation – leaf litter and other organic matter is decomposed (*humification*) and incorporated into the A horizon. The breakdown of organic material releases organic acids, which act as chelating agents and help to breakdown clays into soluble iron and aluminium oxides (sesquioxides).

3 Organic sorting – earthworms and other soil biota help to aggregate soil particles into peds.
4 Translocation – several types of soil material are moved through the soil profile, either downwards if precipitation exceeds evapotranspiration, or upwards if evapotranspiration exceeds precipitation, as for example in arid regions. In the British Isles the major types of translocation are:

■ *Leaching* – the movement of soluble bases (e.g. calcium, magnesium and potassium) down through the profile.
■ *Lessivage* (*eluviation*) – the movement in suspension of clay particles.
■ *Podsolisation* – the removal of iron and aluminium oxides from the A horizon and their redeposition in the B horizon.
■ *Gleying* – occurs when a soil horizon becomes waterlogged, resulting in anaerobic or reducing conditions. It may occur as a groundwater gley, when the watertable rises, or as a surface water gley if water is unable to drain down through the soil profile.

Other types of translocation occur outside the British Isles and include:
■ *Ferrallitisation* – the removal, from the A horizon, of silica in solution, allowing iron and aluminium oxides to accumulate.
■ *Salinisation* – the upward movement of salts in solution, to be deposited either in the A horizon or at the surface.
■ *Calcification* – the redeposition of calcium in the B horizon.

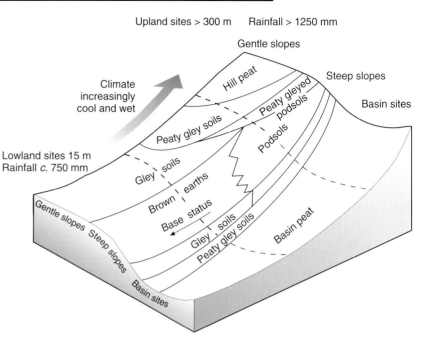

FIGURE 1.2.10 The influence of climate and relief on soil type

Zonal, azonal and intrazonal soil types

If a soil has had time to develop into a 'mature' soil, with distinctive soil horizons, it is then possible to identify, across the major continents, broad *zonal* soil groups which occur in close association with specific climatic and vegetation types. For example, some areas with podsolic soils occur together with a cold temperate climate and coniferous forest.

FIGURE 1.2.11 Zonal soils of the World

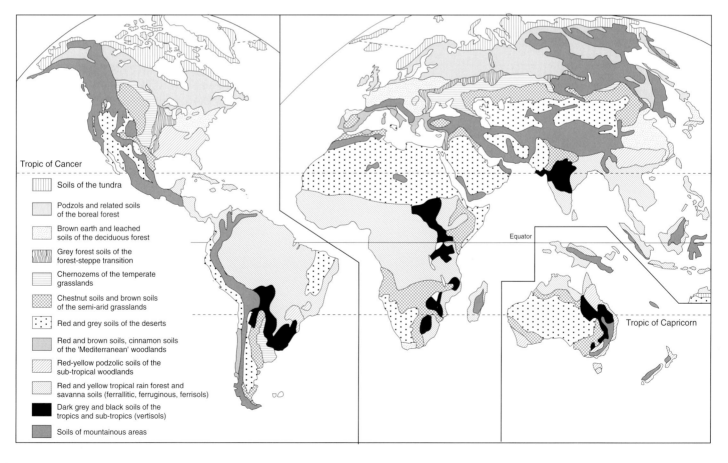

Tropic of Cancer

- Soils of the tundra
- Podzols and related soils of the boreal forest
- Brown earth and leached soils of the deciduous forest
- Grey forest soils of the forest-steppe transition
- Chernozems of the temperate grasslands
- Chestnut soils and brown soils of the semi-arid grasslands
- Red and grey soils of the deserts
- Red and brown soils, cinnamon soils of the 'Mediterranean' woodlands
- Red-yellow podzolic soils of the sub-tropical woodlands
- Red and yellow tropical rain forest and savanna soils (ferrallitic, ferruginous, ferrisols)
- Dark grey and black soils of the tropics and sub-tropics (vertisols)
- Soils of mountainous areas

If a soil is immature, and has not had time to develop, as would be the case near to an active volcano, the result is an *azonal* soil. Some soils, termed *intrazonal* soils, occur within areas of zonal soils where one particular soil forming factor is dominant. They include:

■ *Halomorphic* soils – formed, in arid and tropical savanna areas, as a result of the deposition of salts through salinisation.
■ *Hydromorphic* soils – these occur when the soil is waterlogged, and may be either gley, or peat hydromorphic soils.

■ *Calcimorphic* soils – develop on limestone parent rock and are characterised, in the case of the rendzina soil type, by not possessing a B horizon.

STUDENT ACTIVITY 1.8

Essay: To what extent are soils influenced by relief and climate? (refer to Figure 1.2.10).

CASE STUDY

Lake Gormire and Garbutt Wood

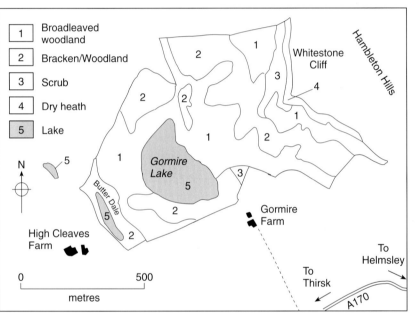

FIGURE 1.2.12 The major habitats of the Gormire-Garbutt Wood SSSI

The Gormire Site of Special Scientific Interest (SSSI) illustrates how, in a small area, there are a wide range of plant communities, closely linked to differences in soil conditions. It is located at the western edge of the North York Moors National Park in North Yorkshire, and was declared a SSSI in 1954.

Topography

The site is part of the western scarp of the Hambleton Hills. It consists of an outlier of the main escarpment to the west, a central valley at approximately 150 metres containing Lake Gormire and the impressive scarp slope to the east rising to 300 metres.

Geology

The geology of the area consists of a sequence of Jurassic rocks. In the west they are mainly shales and sandstones with more resistant gritstones and oolitic limestones forming the main scarp slope.

FIGURE 1.2.13 Lake Gormire

Climate

	Jan	Feb	Mar	Apl	May	June	July	Aug	Sep	Oct	Nov	Dec	
Rainfall mm	75	61	50	52	59	55	71	91	74	67	84	69	Total 808 mm
Temp °C	2	3	5	7	10	13	15	14	13	10	6	4	Range 13°C
PET mm	0	8	27	48	71	80	80	63	39	19	3	0	Total 438 mm

FIGURE 1.2.14 The climate of Gormire SSSI

Soils

Most of the major British soil types are found in this small area, providing a good example of the complex interrelationships between slope angle, climate, rock type, and the nature of the vegetation.

Most of the area covered by deciduous woodland has a brown earth soil type. Where sandstones create more acidic conditions and support bracken an azonal soil type called a ranker occurs. Where limestones are dominant, creating more alkaline conditions, as is the case on the dip slope in the east, another type of azonal soil is found called a rendzina. Both of these soil types do not possess a B horizon. The heath area at the top of the scarp has a typical humus-iron podsol. The wetter areas around the lake have gleyed (waterlogged) soils (Figure 1.2.15).

Plant communities

As would be expected in an area with such a range of habitats, there is a corresponding range of plant communities.

The major community on the slopes is semi-natural deciduous woodland, composed of oak, birch, hazel, sycamore, elm and ash. Beneath the canopy is a ground cover, which includes bluebell, wood sorrel, moschatel foxgloves, wood sage, red campion and broad buckler fern. Bracken also covers large areas, and is an invasive plant, which the management authorities are attempting to eliminate.

The lake has a community consisting of water horsetail, bottle sedge, reedmace, bog bean, and tufted loosestrife. On the lake edge is a marsh community with bog moss, common cotton grass, white sedge, common sedge, and marsh cinquefoil. At the eastern end of the lake are water mint, common skull cap, lesser marshwort, marsh speedwell, and the common spotted orchid.

Above the steep outcrop of Whitestone Cliff is a dry heath community, with bilberry, heather, wavy hair grass, and heath bedstraw.

WEST **EAST**

FIGURE 1.2.15 Soils of the Gormire SSSI

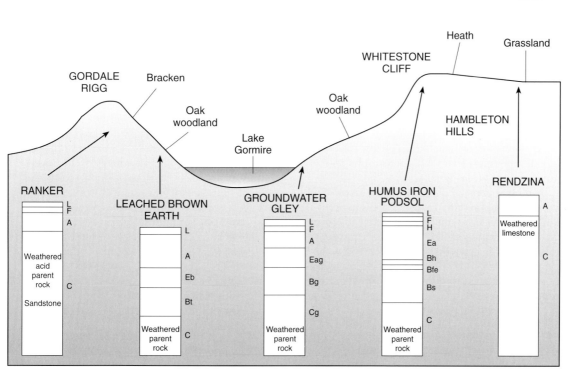

FIGURE 1.2.16 Fieldwork
techniques

Abiotic structure – microclimate and soils		Biotic structure – plants and animals	
Light	Light meter	Number of plant (flora) species	Quadrat/line transect
Temperature (max/min)	Thermometer	Perc. cover of species present	Quadrat/line transect
Wind speed	Anemometer	Vegetation density (distance apart)	Tape
Moisture and humus	Laboratory equipment	Stratification (height of layers)	Tape or metre rule
Temperature	Thermometer	Biomass amount	Scales
pH	pH meter or BDH kit	Number of animal (fauna) species	Animal traps/nets
Depth	Soil auger		
Texture	Sieves		
Infiltration rate	Funnel and water		

STUDENT ACTIVITY 1.9

1 Use the data in Figure 1.2.14 to produce a water budget graph.
2 How will the variations in moisture availability affect the plant community?

STUDENT ACTIVITY 1.10

Use the information in Figure 1.2.16 to help you outline a programme of fieldwork to analyse the structure of the ecosystems in the Gormire – Garbutt Wood SSSI.

1.3 The Functions of Ecosystems

The two major functions within an ecosystem are the transfer of energy *through*, and the recycling of nutrients *within* the ecosystem.

Energy Flows in Ecosystems – Photosynthesis

Photosynthesis (or phototrophism) is the process by which light energy from the sun (insolation), is absorbed by plants, blue-green algae and certain bacteria. It is then used to produce new plant cell material, which forms the food source for plant eating animals (herbivores).

Plants which are able, through the process of photosynthesis, to convert light energy and inorganic substances (carbon dioxide, water and various mineral nutrients) into organic (carbon based) molecules, are called **phototrophs** or **autotrophs** ('self-feeders').

In a plant, most photosynthesis is carried out by the leaves, and in order for the process to occur they must contain chlorophyll, which is able to absorb energy from sunlight. The plant also requires carbon dioxide, from the atmosphere, and water from the soil. As a result of the process, oxygen is released, as a waste product, and carbohydrates are produced.

$$6CO_2 \quad + \quad 12H_2O \rightarrow C_6H_{12}O_6 + 6O_2 + 6H_2O$$
carbon dioxide water   glucose oxygen water

The carbohydrates produced by photosynthesis are:

1 Combined with elements such as nitrogen, phosphorous and sulphur to produce proteins and nucleic acids.

2 Converted into starch and stored in the plant.
3 Converted into cellulose (the main plant structural material).
4 Used by the plant for **respiration** i.e. biochemical processes, cell maintenance and growth.

Most plants follow the C3 photosynthesis pathway, but some including tropical and subtropical grasses, and several crop plants such as maize, sorghum, sugar cane and millet follow the C4 pathway. C4 plants have a very high efficiency of CO_2 fixing, and a very efficient level of water use. They are able to continue to carry out photosynthesis even when their stomata are partially closed. They are adapted to survive under saline conditions, and are more tolerant of dry conditions. Some desert succulent cacti and tropical epiphyte plants (orchids) follow the CAM pathway. Organic acids are produced during the night, to take advantage of the lower temperatures when the stomata open, which then close during the day when temperatures are higher.

Levels of photosynthesis vary considerably. As photosynthesis is a multi-stage process, involving the interaction of several factors, it can be limited by the one factor, which is nearest to its minimum value, this is known as 'The Law of the Minimum'. The limiting factors which affect the rate of photosynthesis are temperature, light intensity, carbon dioxide concentration and the availability of water.

Energy flow through an ecosystem

The energy produced by photosynthesis will pass through the food chains and food webs of an ecosystem, with some of it being stored as chemical

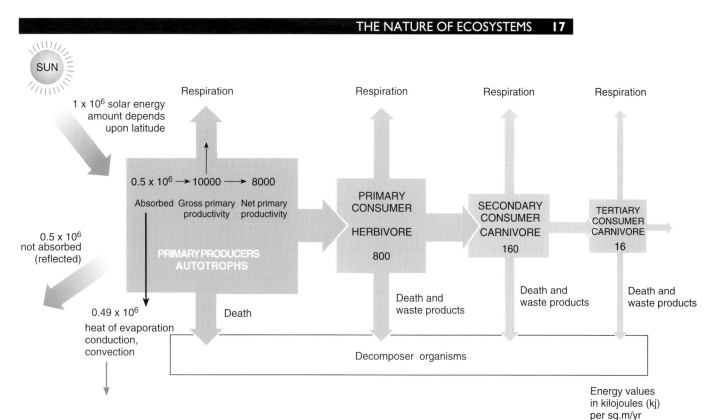

SUN

1×10^6 solar energy
amount depends
upon latitude

Respiration   Respiration   Respiration   Respiration

$0.5 \times 10^6 \longrightarrow 10000 \longrightarrow 8000$

Absorbed Gross primary Net primary
          productivity   productivity

**PRIMARY PRODUCERS
AUTOTROPHS**

PRIMARY
CONSUMER

HERBIVORE

800

SECONDARY
CONSUMER
CARNIVORE

160

TERTIARY
CONSUMER
CARNIVORE

16

0.5×10^6
not absorbed
(reflected)

0.49×10^6
heat of evaporation
conduction,
convection

Death

Death and
waste products

Death and
waste products

Death and
waste products

Decomposer organisms

Energy values
in kilojoules (kj)
per sq.m/yr

FIGURE 1.3.1 Energy flow
through an ecosystem

energy in plant and animal tissue. Some of it will be lost from the system, as respiration (heat energy) and excreta products. The total amount of energy lost, from all the trophic levels in an ecosystem through respiration, forms the *community respiration*. Energy is lost at each level in the food chain, with the average efficiency of transfer from plants to herbivores being about 10 per cent, and about 20 per cent from animal to animal (Figure 1.3.1).

As a result of the loss of energy at each transfer between trophic levels, ecosystems are usually limited to three or four trophic levels. The actual number will depend upon the size of the initial autotroph (producer) biomass, and the efficiency of energy transfer between the trophic levels.

Nutrient (gaseous and biogeochemical) cycles

The nutrients, or elements used by all organisms for growth and reproduction, are termed *essential elements* or macronutrients, and include carbon (C), hydrogen (H), oxygen (O), nitrogen (N), phosphorus (P), sodium (Na), sulphur (S), chlorine (Cl), potassium (K), calcium (Ca) and magnesium (Mg). Other elements called *trace elements* or micronutrients, including iron (Fe), manganese (Mn), copper (Cu), zinc (Zn) and cobalt (Co), are also required, but in smaller quantities. Some organisms also require molybdenum (Mo), silica (Si), and boron (B).

The nutrients required by plants are obtained as inputs either from the atmosphere through various *gaseous* cycles or in precipitation, or from the soil via the weathering of parent rock, through several *biogeochemical* or *sedimentary* cycles. The two types

of cycle are interrelated, as nutrients pass from abiotic nutrient stores, such as the soil and the atmosphere, into biotic, plant and animal stores (the biomass). The nutrients are then recycled, within the ecosystem, following death and decomposition (Figure 1.3.2). Nutrients are lost, as outputs, by surface runoff, leaching through the soil profile or the removal of plant, animal, leaf litter or soil material. The concept of the recycling of nutrients between three compartments or stores is shown in Gersmehl's Model (Figure 3.1.5).

FIGURE 1.3.2 Simplified
model of the
biogeochemical nutrient
cycle

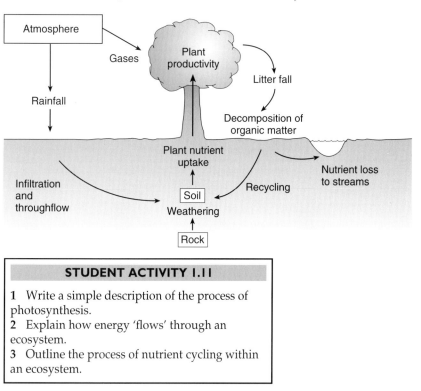

Atmosphere

Gases

Plant
productivity

Litter fall

Rainfall

Decomposition of
organic matter

Plant nutrient
uptake

Nutrient loss
to streams

Infiltration
and
throughflow

Soil

Recycling

Weathering

Rock

STUDENT ACTIVITY 1.11

1 Write a simple description of the process of photosynthesis.
2 Explain how energy 'flows' through an ecosystem.
3 Outline the process of nutrient cycling within an ecosystem.

1.4 Productivity and Global Patterns

GPP, NPP and Biomass

The productivity of an ecosystem refers to its autotrophs, or primary producer's ability, to produce organic matter, normally in the form of plant material. As such, it depends upon the level of photosynthesis, which in turn reflects the levels of available solar energy (light), temperature, moisture, nutrients and carbon dioxide. Productivity can be expressed as either gross or net primary productivity. Gross primary productivity (GPP) is a measure of the total amount of energy fixed by the primary producers. Net primary productivity (NPP) is the GPP minus respiration (the amount of energy converted to heat or used in life processes by the producers):

NPP = GPP − Respiration

The NPP is the rate of accumulation of living material, in a given area, over a certain period of time, and is normally expressed, in grams per square metre per year (g/sq.m/yr). The biomass is the total amount of living material found in a given area.

FIGURE 1.4.1 The productivity of the major biomes of the World

Global Differences in Productivity

Figure 1.4.1 illustrates a classification of land biomes based on their net primary productivity. As may be seen there is a clear link between productivity levels and climate. The highest mean land based NPP figure, 2200 g/sq.m/yr, is found in tropical rain forest areas, where high temperatures and moisture availability throughout the year result in a potential 365 growing days. The very low figure of 3 g/sq.m/yr, in extreme arid areas, clearly indicates the effect of a lack of available moisture despite high levels of insolation.

Similarly, the importance of tropical rain forests is indicated by its biomass total of 765 000 m tonnes, out of a world land total of 1837 1000 m tonnes, representing a staggering 42 per cent.

STUDENT ACTIVITY 1.12

1 Refer to Figure 1.4.1 and plot the Net Primary Productivity and Mean Annual Solar Radiation data as a scattergraph.
2 Use a statistical technique, such as the Spearman correlation coefficient, to calculate the relationship between the two sets of data.
3 Use both the scattergraph and the correlation coefficient to analyse the relationship between the two sets of data.

	Biome	Mean Net Primary Productivity (g/sq.m/year)	Mean Biomass (kg/sq.m)	World biomass (thousand million tonnes)	Mean annual solar radiation (W/sq.m/year)
High Energy	Tropical Evergreen Forests	2200	45	765	175
	Tropical Seasonal Forests	1600	35	260	200
	Temperate Deciduous Forests	1200	30	210	125
Average Energy	Tropical Savanna Grasslands	900	4	60	225
	Temperate Coniferous Forests	800	35	175	100
	Temperate Grassland	600	1.6	14	150
Low Energy	Tundra and Alpine	140	0.6	5	90
	Tropical Desert	90	0.7	13	250
	Extreme Desert, Rock, Polar	3	0.02	0.5	75
	Continental Average	773	12.3	Total 1837	156

1.5 Agro-ecosystems

Natural ecosystems	Agro-ecosystems
High diversity of plants and animals	Low diversity of species
Complex structure with well developed food webs	Simple structure
Producers (autotrophs) form the largest biomass component	Consumers (heterotrophs) form the largest biomass component
A large amount of the ecosystem's energy reaches the decomposers	The removal of plant and animal crops reduces the amount of energy available for the decomposers
A large amount of the ecosystem's nutrients are recycled	Natural nutrients are removed, and the nutrient cycle is maintained by the addition of chemical (inorganic) fertilisers
Solar energy and nutrients from weathered rock are the major inputs	More open, with a larger input into, and output of material from the system
Variable net primary productivity related to changes in insolation and nutrients	Farmers attempt to maintain productivity by the addition of moisture, fertilisers, etc.

FIGURE 1.5.1 The differences between natural and agro-ecosystems

Throughout the world there are many different types of agriculture including subsistence, commercial, intensive, extensive, arable and pastoral. Each type has a unique impact upon its environment with, generally, the degree of the impact increasing with the intensity of agriculture, and the increasing use of technology. Agriculture may be seen as the creation of artificial or modified ecosystems, which can be called agro-ecosystems. Generally, agro-ecosystems simplify natural ecosystems by concentrating only on a few species of crops and animals. This can make the system more unstable, and prone to change through the effects of pests, diseases or climatic change. Other differences between natural and agro-ecosystems are illustrated in Figure 1.5.1.

The Structure of Agro-ecosystems

It is possible to identify four major types of agro-ecosystems, each of which has its own specific environmental or abiotic requirements:

1 Cultivated (tillage) crop (producers) → human consumption (primary consumers i.e. herbivores).

2 Cultivated (tillage) crop (producers) → livestock (primary consumers i.e. herbivores) → human consumption of (meat and dairy products) (secondary consumers i.e. carnivores).

3 Grassland (producers) → livestock (primary consumers i.e. herbivores) → human consumption of meat and dairy products (secondary consumers i.e. carnivores).

4 Grassland and crops (mixed agriculture) (producers) → livestock (primary consumers i.e. herbivores) → human consumption (of meat and dairy products (secondary consumers i.e. carnivores)

Energy and Nutrient Flows in Agro-ecosystems

One of the major aims of agro-ecosystems is to increase either the crop or animal biomass. In order to achieve this, genetics and biotechnology have developed new high yielding varieties (HYV) of the major crops and more productive livestock breeds. These require large quantities of fertilisers, pesticides and herbicides (weedkillers), all of which have used energy during their manufacture by industrial processes. The increasing use of machinery, both on the farm and in the distribution of agricultural products, to a variety of markets, adds considerably to the total energy consumed. This type of energy has been described as subsidiary or commercial energy. It is possible to convert all the energy inputs into agro-ecosystems, into energy values.

FIGURE 1.5.2 Shifting cultivation in Amazonia

STUDENT ACTIVITY 1.13

1 Explain the differences between natural and agro-ecosystems with respect to their:
a) structure
b) energy flow, and
c) nutrient cycling.
2 Compare the impact of the two farming systems illustrated in Figures 1.5.2 and 1.5.3 on the original natural ecosystem.

---

then released into the soil. The nutrients are then recycled slowly between the soil, the biomass, and the leaf litter, with a small loss through surface run-off.

In an agro-ecosystem, much of the surface biomass is removed as a crop, breaking the natural nutrient cycle. To supplement this loss, nutrients are added by the farmer, either as organic fertiliser (farmyard manure) or, increasingly, as manufactured inorganic fertiliser. The lack of organic matter being returned to the soil decreases

The energy use of different agro-ecosystems may be analysed by reference to the energy efficiency ratio (EER), which is calculated by:

$$EER = \frac{\text{Food output (energy per hectare)}}{\text{Energy input (per hectare)}}$$

In a natural ecosystem, the principal nutrient sources are either from the atmosphere, or from nutrients derived from the weathering of rock and

---

STUDENT ACTIVITY 1.14

Refer to Figure 1.5.4 and:
1 Calculate the EER for shifting cultivation and the USA corn belt.
2 Explain the significance of the different values of the EER.

FIGURE 1.5.4 Energy efficiency of various agro-ecosystems

Farming system	Energy input hectare MJ	% of energy from fossil fuels	Energy output hectare MJ	Energy efficiency ratio
Shifting cultivation(cassava)	103	0	1460	
S. India trad. Rice cult.	3255	58	42 280	12.99
S. India HYV Rice cult.	6878	77	66 460	9.66
UK mixed farm	21 870	97	44 890	2.05
USA corn belt	29 850	99	76 910	
Energy efficiency ratios for crops and livestock in the USA				
Oats 2.70	Wheat 3.44	Beef (rangeland) 10.1	Milk 35.9	Beef (feed-lot) 77.7

FIGURE 1.5.3 Upland rice cultivation in the Philippines

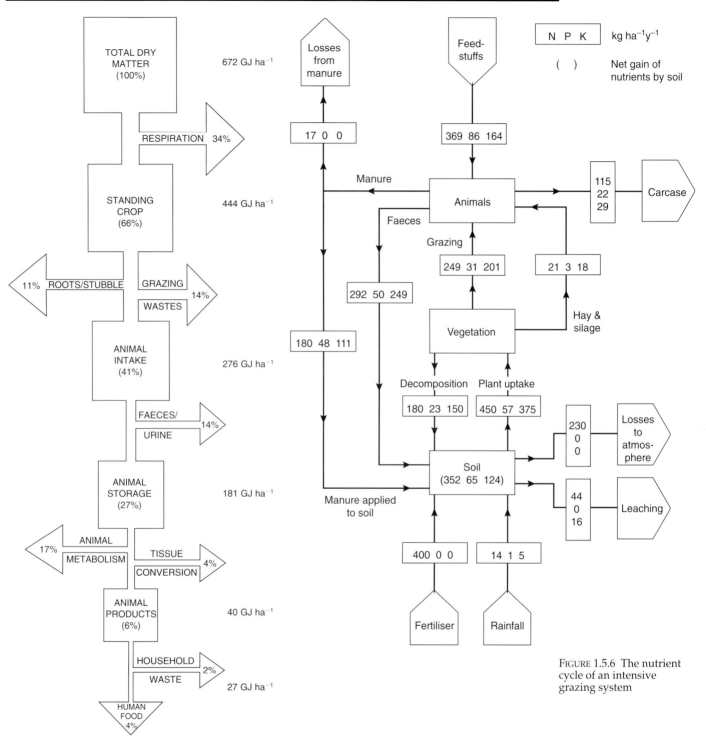

FIGURE 1.5.5 The energy efficiency of a typical intensive grazing system. The total dry matter produced in the system is about 672 GJ/ha/yr, which is only 0.5 per cent of solar radiation inputs. The human food produced is only about 0.02 per cent of the amount of solar energy received.

FIGURE 1.5.6 The nutrient cycle of an intensive grazing system

the amount of humus in the soil, which in turn affects the soil's ability to hold certain nutrients. In the wet climates of temperate areas, it is then very easy for inorganic fertilisers to be lost, by leaching, through the soil profile. This may well then lead to problems of chemical pollution, especially by nitrates, in rivers and lakes (Chapter 5). The soil structure is also affected, as the organic materials helps to bind together the soil particles (or peds). A lack of humus will mean that the soil is more susceptible to soil erosion by both the wind (aeolian) and by rain (surface run-off) (Chapters 4 and 5).

2

DYNAMIC
ECOSYSTEMS

Key Ideas

- Ecosystems may exist in a relatively stable state, or may be subject to change through natural processes, or the influence of human activities.
- The development of a plant succession from bare ground is called a prisere. The main types of prisere include xeroseres, haloseres, psammoseres and hydroseres.

- Plant and animal populations fluctuate over time, and may be analysed by various models.
- There are several different types of interactions between the populations within the ecosystem community and its natural environment.
- Palaeoecology is the study of how ecosystems have changed over pre-historical time.

2.1 Colonisation and Succession

Primary Successions

When a bare land surface is exposed, for example after a volcanic eruption or the retreat of a glacier, it is quickly colonised by a plant community which changes over time producing a *primary plant succession*. Each plant community in the succession is called a **sere** or seral community, and a sequence of seres over time forms a primary succession or **prisere**. Several stages may be identified in a typical prisere (Figure 2.1.1). The arrival of seeds and spores on the land surface allows the growth of the pioneer or colonising sere, and gradually over time this is replaced by more complex communities. The pioneer species depends to some degree upon the nature of the land surface (substrate), lichens colonise smooth bare rock, mosses and liverworts (bryophytes) ribbed rock, ferns and trees on block scree, perennial herbs on gravel, and grasses on sands. The traditional view, proposed in 1916 by F E Clements, was that the prisere would eventually lead to a climatic **climax community**, where the plant community was in dynamic equilibrium with

its environment (Figure 2.1.2). This theory of a linear sequence of seres is known as the *mono-climax* concept. An alternative theory, the *polyclimax* concept, accepts that several factors such as parent rock, soil condition, drainage, fire and topography also need to be considered.

Some ecologists believe that the idea of a 'plant community', developing as a whole, is too simplistic. Instead, they believe that the community develops as a continuum, with individual plant species developing and declining over time, in response not only to abiotic factors but also to competition from other plants and the effects of herbivores. This concept can be studied by *gradient analysis*, which graphs the distribution of different species over time (Figure 2.1.3).

Primary successions are characterised by the initial surface having no pre-existing seed bank, or residue of vegetative means of reproduction. Species migrate into the area to colonise the bare surface. Soil forming processes begin to convert the

FIGURE 2.1.1 Seral stages in a primary succession (prisere)

Seral stage	Activities
1 Colonisation	Pioneer r-species develop as seeds and spores arrive on the land surface
2 Establishment	Species diversity increases
3 Competition	Equilibrium K-species replace pioneers. Competition for space, light, water and nutrients
4 Stabilisation	Fewer new species arrive
5 Climax	Final plant community in equilibrium with its environment

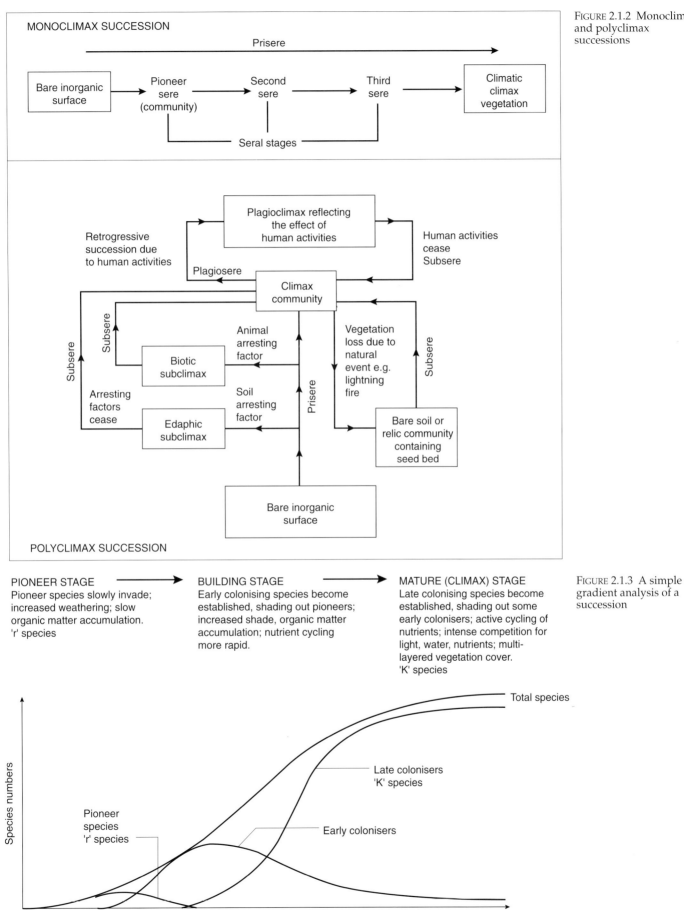

MONOCLIMAX SUCCESSION

Prisere

Bare inorganic surface → Pioneer sere (community) → Second sere → Third sere → Climatic climax vegetation

Seral stages

Retrogressive succession due to human activities

Plagioclimax reflecting the effect of human activities

Human activities cease
Subsere

Plagiosere

Climax community

Subsere

Subsere

Arresting factors cease

Biotic subclimax

Animal arresting factor

Edaphic subclimax

Soil arresting factor

Prisere

Vegetation loss due to natural event e.g. lightning fire

Subsere

Bare soil or relic community containing seed bed

Bare inorganic surface

POLYCLIMAX SUCCESSION

FIGURE 2.1.2 Monoclimax and polyclimax successions

PIONEER STAGE ⟶ Pioneer species slowly invade; increased weathering; slow organic matter accumulation. 'r' species

BUILDING STAGE ⟶ Early colonising species become established, shading out pioneers; increased shade, organic matter accumulation; nutrient cycling more rapid.

MATURE (CLIMAX) STAGE Late colonising species become established, shading out some early colonisers; active cycling of nutrients; intense competition for light, water, nutrients; multi-layered vegetation cover. 'K' species

FIGURE 2.1.3 A simple gradient analysis of a succession

Species numbers

Total species

Late colonisers 'K' species

Pioneer species 'r' species

Early colonisers

Time

VEGETATION COVER

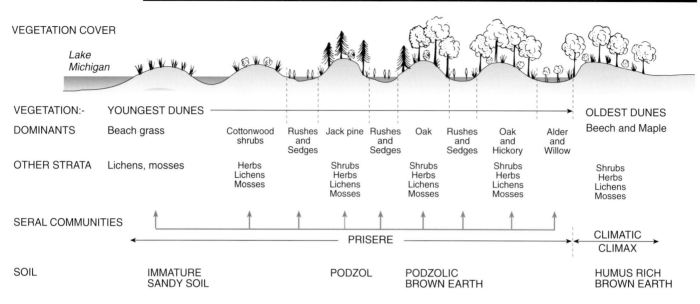

VEGETATION:-	YOUNGEST DUNES									OLDEST DUNES
DOMINANTS	Beach grass	Cottonwood shrubs	Rushes and Sedges	Jack pine	Rushes and Sedges	Oak	Rushes and Sedges	Oak and Hickory	Alder and Willow	Beech and Maple
OTHER STRATA	Lichens, mosses	Herbs Lichens Mosses		Shrubs Herbs Lichens Mosses		Shrubs Herbs Lichens Mosses		Shrubs Herbs Lichens Mosses		Shrubs Herbs Lichens Mosses

SERAL COMMUNITIES

PRISERE · CLIMATIC CLIMAX

SOIL	IMMATURE SANDY SOIL	PODZOL	PODZOLIC BROWN EARTH	HUMUS RICH BROWN EARTH

FIGURE 2.1.4 Plant succession and soil type on the dunes of Lake Michigan

inorganic regolith into soil, through the addition of organic material. On land, as the primary succession develops, it is associated with increasing soil nitrogen, increasing organic matter, and increase in the height of the mature plants. Early colonising plants are often vascular plants, such as legumes and other nitrogen fixing species. For example on naturally colonised china clay wastes in Devon and Cornwall, tree lupins are able to add 72 kg ha per year of nitrogen, and gorse can add 27 kg ha per year.

The type of prisere depends upon the initial surface. Land surfaces produce *xeroseres* (low moisture) which are either *lithoseres* when formed on bare rock or *psammoseres* if on sand dunes. Fresh water areas, such as ponds and lakes are colonised through a *hydrosere*, and sea water through a *halosere*. The primary successions outlined above are examples of *autogenic* succession, where the plant community itself controls the succession by altering the environmental conditions of the habitat. In the south of the British Isles, it is possible that all of them could eventually lead to a climatic climax consisting of oak woodland (Figure 2.1.5).

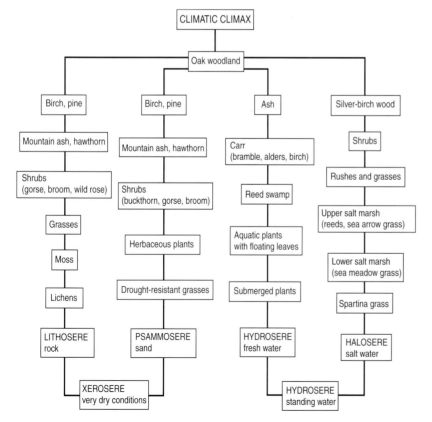

STUDENT ACTIVITY 2.1

1 Define the terms: sere, prisere, climax, plagioclimax and subsere.
2 Outline the differences between the *monoclimax*, *polyclimax* and *gradient analysis* approaches to understanding plant succession.

On some occasions the development of a prisere may be stopped or 'arrested' by either soil (edaphic) conditions, for example waterlogging, or biotic factors such as overgrazing, or attacks by locusts and other insects. This will result in a **subclimax** community being formed. Once the limiting or arresting factor is removed the community will develop through a **subsere** to the climax community.

FIGURE 2.1.5 Prisere successions leading to an oak climax community

Secondary Successions

Under some circumstances the original primary succession may be affected by processes, which are 'external' to the plant community, for example fire, landslide or flooding. This produces instability in the system, with the partial or total destruction of the original plant cover, and results in the creation of a secondary or *allogenic* succession. This is usually lower in height and less diverse than the original ecosystem. Human activities, including grazing, arable farming and deforestation, are a major cause of secondary successions and lead to a deflected or **plagioclimax** community. If the human activities cease, the plagioclimax community will eventually, through a subsere, evolve into a climatic climax community.

Secondary successions begin with a more or less mature soil, containing a large bank of seeds, and vegetative methods of reproduction. The succession usually begins with short lived pioneer plants, followed by herbaceous perennials. They are often replaced by short lived trees, which in turn are succeeded by the long living dominant trees.

STUDENT ACTIVITY 2.2

1 With reference to Figure 2.1.4 describe how the plant communities change inland.
2 What is the relationship between the changes in the plant communities and the nature of the soil?

CASE STUDY

Plant succession after a volcanic eruption: Krakatoa

After a volcano has ceased to erupt, conditions are ideal to investigate how the volcanic rocks, lava and ash, are weathered and colonised by plants.

Krakatoa
On Monday, the 27th of August, in 1883, two-thirds (over 20 sq km) of the island of Krakatoa, situated in the ocean between Java and Sumatra, was destroyed by a massive volcanic eruption. In Java and Sumatra, 36 000 people were killed by tidal waves (tsunamis) produced as a result of the eruption. Figure 2.1.6 provides details of the plant and animal succession on the island. As can be seen the rate of colonisation has been very rapid. After only ten years large areas were covered by savanna

grasses and the occasional tree, and within 100 years the lower slopes had reached a type of equatorial forest climax. The reasons for this rapid rate of colonisation are believed to be:

1 The presence nearby of numerous islands with a wide diversity of species, which were able to reach Krakatoa by sea (60 per cent of species), by winds (32 per cent), and by birds (8 per cent).
2 The high temperatures and regular rainfall of this equatorial area are ideal for plant growth.
3 The volcanic soils quickly weather under these climatic conditions releasing mineral nutrients.

STUDENT ACTIVITY 2.3

Analyse the vegetation changes that have occurred on Krakatoa since 1883.

FIGURE 2.1.6 Succession on Krakatoa

Year	No. of plant species	No. of animal species	Coast	Lower slopes	Upper slopes
1883	0		Volcanic eruption, all life killed		
1886	26		Nine species of flowering plants	Ferns and scattered flowers, blue-green algae on ash	
1897	64		Beach plants	Dense grasses	Mosses and ferns
1908	115	200	Wider belt of woodland with more species, and coconut palms	Dense grasses up to 3 metres high, woodland in ravines	Mosses, ferns some grasses and shrubs
1918	132		Wider belt of woodland with more species, and coconut palms	Scattered trees in savanna grassland with woodland in ravines	Mosses, shrubs, ferns and orchids
1921	142	618			
1933	271	795	Coastal woodland climax	Mixed woodland largely replaces grasses	Mosses, shrubs, ferns and orchids, woodland in ravines
1997	?	?		Rainforest climax	

CASE STUDY

Plant succession after the retreat of a glacier

Approximately 10 000 years ago, the glacial conditions of the Pleistocene, which had covered Britain for over 2 m years, were replaced by the higher temperatures of the *Holocene* or *Recent* inter-glacial. As the glaciers retreated the land surface was quickly colonised by vegetation. It has been possible to reconstruct the plant succession over the last 10 000 years by studying fossil pollen found preserved in peat deposits. The study of pollen and its related environmental conditions is termed **palynology**, a branch of **palaeoecology** (the study of ancient environments and their life forms). In the *anaerobic* or low oxygen conditions, which are found in peat bogs, pollen is remarkably resistant to decay. Each layer of peat represents a period of

time, from the oldest at the base of the deposit to the youngest at the surface. Once the pollen has been identified and dated, it is possible to produce a sequence of the plant succession for the site from where the pollen was obtained. As numerous pollen sites have now been studied, it is possible to divide the period since the end of the last Devensian glaciation into distinctive pollen zones (Figure 2.1.7).

STUDENT ACTIVITY 2.4

Refer to Figure 2.1.7, and describe and explain the changes that have occurred in England's vegetation since the last glacial period.

FIGURE 2.1.7 Vegetation succession in England since the last glacial period

Pollen zone	Name/Date	Climate	Dominant vegetation
VIII	Sub-Atlantic 500 BC	Maritime: cooler and wetter	Oak forests cleared as agriculture increases
VIIb	Sub-Boreal 3000 BC	Continental: warmer and drier	Oak and heathers
VIIa	Atlantic 6000 BC	Maritime: Climatic optimum	Alder, oak, elm and lime
VIc		Cold temperate continental:	
VIb	Boreal	colder winters and warmer	Scots pine and birch
VIa	8000 BC	summers	
IV	Pre-Boreal 10 000 BC	Tundra	Birch
III	Upper Dryas 11 000 BC	Tundra/Glacial	Birch
II	Allerod	Tundra/Glacial	Birch

CASE STUDY

Malham Tarn

Malham Tarn National Nature Reserve in the Yorkshire Dales National Park has both a unique history, providing a good example of plant succession and a wide range of habitats (Figure 2.1.8).

Succession

Throughout most of this part of the Yorkshire Dales National Park, the dominant rock is Carboniferous Limestone. However, as a result of earth movements, older impermeable Silurian slates appear at the surface in the Malham Tarn area. This Silurian surface was eroded by the ice during the last (Devensian) glacial period, producing numerous depressions. It was in one of these, which was also dammed by glacial deposits, that glacial meltwaters accumulated eventually forming the lake which is now Malham Tarn.

Initially, the bed of the Tarn was covered in silt, eroded and deposited by streams draining into the Tarn from the surrounding glacial deposits. The main feeder stream, in the west, now flows over limestone, and consequently has a high calcium carbonate content. Over a very long period of time calcium carbonate, brought into the Tarn by surface streams, has precipitated out and has accumulated on the bed of the Tarn. To this has been added material from submerged plants, such as stonewort, together with the shells of molluscs, including the pea mussel eventually forming a lime rich lake deposit called a marl.

Phosphorus is precipitated out from the lake water, and this has the effect of limiting the growth of phyto-plankton in the Tarn. Plants, such as stonewort, however, with roots on the bed of the lake, have access to a rich supply.

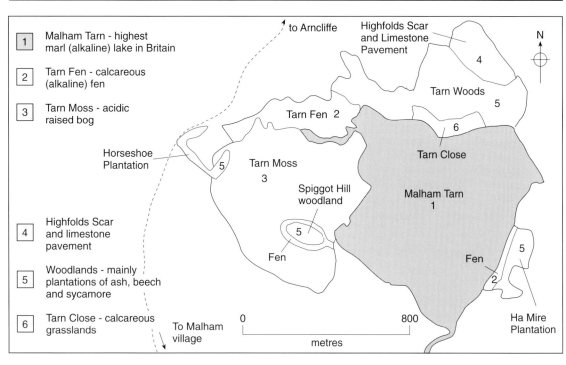

FIGURE 2.1.8 Habitats of the Malham Tarn National Nature Reserve

1　Malham Tarn - highest marl (alkaline) lake in Britain

2　Tarn Fen - calcareous (alkaline) fen

3　Tarn Moss - acidic raised bog

4　Highfolds Scar and limestone pavement

5　Woodlands - mainly plantations of ash, beech and sycamore

6　Tarn Close - calcareous grasslands

FIGURE 2.1.9 The Management of the Malham Tarn National Nature Reserve

Habitat	Environmental Problem	Management Solution
Malham Tarn	Acid rain Pollution from car exhausts Pollution from salt run off from roads Pollution from agricultural run off	Water quality frequently monitored for pollution Local septic tanks upgraded Environmentally friendly farming encouraged around the Tarn
Malham Fen	Acid rain Pollution from salt run off from roads Pollution from agricultural run off Invasion of willow scrub	Pools regularly cleared Willow scrub cleared Protection of lime rich springs and streams draining into the fen
Malham Moss	Lowering of water table	Old drainage ditches blocked to maintain water level
Malham Woodland	Acid Rain Introduction of non-native trees species Excessive shrub growth	Removal of non-native conifers Shrubs removed to open up woodland glades for wildflowers and insects Regeneration of young trees, especially ash, encouraged Dead wood left to decompose to encourage fungi and insects Old broadleaved trees retained

Gradually, along the western shore of the Tarn, at the point where the lime-rich main stream formed a small delta as it flowed into the Tarn, in the area now called Tarn Fen, a calcareous (lime-rich) fen community became established. As the vegetation in parts of the fen decayed, a peaty organic layer was built up which, eventually, was higher than the water table, producing a raised bog community now known as Tarn Moss. This type of bog community is kept moist by rainfall, which at Malham Tarn averages 1473 mm per year. As the rainfall is naturally slightly acidic, it has helped to produce an acidic bog plant community.

Management of the Malham Tarn Nature Reserve

Apart from being a National Nature Reserve, Malham Tarn is also a Site of Special Scientific Interest (SSSI), and a RAMSAR site. RAMSAR status means that it is a protected site because of its importance for such wild birds as curlew, lapwing, redshank, snipe, coot, tufted duck, and great crested grebe.

The Malham Tarn Reserve is owned by the National Trust, who lease part of it to the Field Studies Council for educational and research purposes. The National Trust carries out the management of the reserve.

STUDENT ACTIVITY 2.5

Produce an annotated map to summarise the main features of the various habitats in the Malham Tarn area, and how they are being managed.

2.2 Population Dynamics

A population is group of individuals of a particular plant or animal species in a given area at a particular time. Population dynamics is concerned with how and why populations change over time, in response to other populations and their environments. Population size is determined by the relative rates of births (natality), deaths (mortality), and migration (immigration and emigration).

The actual size of a plant population will be the result of a wide range of factors including:

1 *permissive (abiotic or physical) factors* – including light, temperature, moisture, soil conditions, mineral nutrients, carbon dioxide in the atmosphere, aspect, and,

2 *selective (biotic) factors* – including a plant's range of tolerance, plant dispersal and plant migration, competition from other plants for light, water and nutrients, the effect of animals, defoliating insects, pathogenic fungi, and human activities (including grazing animals, fire, crops, deforestation and pollution).

Population growth curves

Although there are a variety of ways in which populations may grow, three major types can be recognised:

1 *'S' shaped, or sigmoid curve* – This type of growth is characteristic of *'density dependent'* populations. Initial growth rates will be similar to a 'J' curve, but are lower because of the effects of *'environmental resistance'*. This is a term used to describe the abiotic, biotic and population factors which restrict the growth rate. Eventually, as the population density increases, the rate of growth will begin to decline, as for example food sources become limited. The growth curve then 'flattens out' and stabilises producing the 'S' shape. This level of population stability is the *'carrying capacity'*, the

FIGURE 2.2.1 Theoretical population growth curves: (a) the 'S'-curve, (b) the 'J'-curve and (c) cyclical growth

maximum number of the population that can be supported by their environment at a particular time.

2 *'J' shaped* or *'boom and bust'* – In this type of growth a population is often seen to grow exponentially, that is, 2, 4, 8, 16, 32 . . ., over a period of time. When these figures are plotted they produce a 'J' shaped curve, which is very similar to the growth curve of the human population during the past 100 years. Normally, these 'boom' periods of growth are followed by a very quick fall, the 'bust' component. This sequence has been well documented in a study of the deer population of the Kaibob Plateau in Arizona. In 1906 the area was declared a wildlife refuge and the major predators, including wolves, coyotes and pumas were exterminated. This allowed the 1906 deer population of 4000 to increase to 100 000 by 1924. It was estimated that the resources in the area could only support a population of 30 000. Overgrazing followed, seriously damaging the environment and causing the deer population to 'crash' down to 10 000 in 1945. 'J' curves are examples of *'density independent'* growth, because the growth rate of each individual is independent of the overall density of population.

3 *Cyclical growth* – Some populations, for example the heather moth, fluctuate on a regular cycle, in response to changes in climate, predation or food supply.

STUDENT ACTIVITY 2.6

1 Write a summary of the three types of population growth curves.
2 Draw a graph to illustrate the changes in the Kaibob deer population. Draw a line at 30 000, and label it the 'carrying capacity'.
3 How would you expect the population to change over the next 50 years?

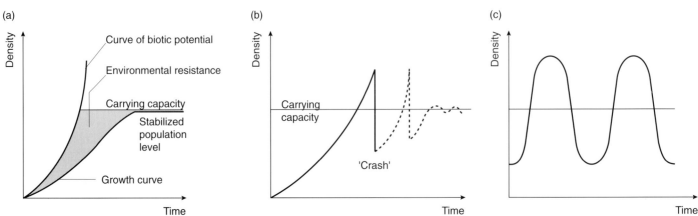

(a)
Density
Curve of biotic potential
Environmental resistance
Carrying capacity
Stabilized population level
Growth curve
Time

(b)
Density
Carrying capacity
'Crash'
Time

(c)
Density
Time

Characteristic	Stage of ecosystem development	
	Immature (early)	**Mature (late)**
Food chains	short, linear mainly grazing	long, web-like
Gross production/community respiration (P/R ratio)	high (>1)	approaches 1
Biomass (total organic matter)	low	high
Species diversity	low	high
Structure of community	simple	complex (stratification, many microhabitats)
Niche specialisation	broad	narrow
Size of organisms	small	large
Species strategies	'r' strategy	'K' strategy

FIGURE 2.2.2 Ecosystem changes during a typical succession

Population strategies

The aim of each individual in a population is its long term survival. In order to achieve this various strategies are used. The two most widely described are the 'opportunist' or r-species strategy, and the 'competitor or equilibrium' or K-species strategy.

1 *r-species strategy* – Some species, especially those which reproduce rapidly, are able to quickly colonise an area, in other words to take the opportunity of being the pioneer species in a new or disturbed habitat such as bare rock, cleared forest or burnt areas. These species tend to be small and short lived with a population growth curve which follows the 'J' model.

2 *K-species strategy* – These competitor species will gradually replace the earlier pioneer species. K-species tend to be larger, reproduce more slowly but live longer and eventually form the dominants in a stable ecosystem.

The concept of 'r' and 'K' species has been modified by J P Grime to analyse how plants respond to three conditions:

1 The intensity of *disturbance*, that is physical damage to the environment and plants.
2 *Competition* for limited resources, and
3 *Stress*, resulting from poor environmental factors, such as extreme temperatures or poor soil conditions.

STRESS INCREASES e.g. cold, low fertility, low precipitation →

DISTURBANCE INCREASES e.g. grazing, trampling, drought ↓

Competitors	**Stress Tolerators**
Growth is not restricted by stress or disturbance, so productivity is high	High levels of stress limit growth rates
Plants are often large, with an extensive lateral spread	Leaves are often small
A high proportion of nutrients are rapidly incorporated into the vegetative structure	Many plants are evergreen
There is a high turnover of leaves and roots	A high proportion of nutrients are found in storage structures in the leaves, stems and/or roots
Flowers and seeds are generally formed quite late in the growing season	Flowering is intermittent over a long life-span
Example: false oat grass	Examples: cacti, alpines, lichens
Ruderals	
Regular disturbance means that no plants have an extended opportunity for growth	
Leaf production is explosive over a short period	
Plants tend to be small, with a limited lateral spread	**No vegetation**
Flower production is important, and seeds are set early	
Seeds often contain a high proportion of nutrients, and can remain dormant for long periods	
Examples: 'r' species of plants, annual herbs e.g. annual meadow grass	

FIGURE 2.2.3 Grime's plant types

2.3 Interactions

The levels of interaction in an ecosystem depend upon the size of the various populations at each trophic level, and the links between the populations of each trophic level, and the abiotic environment. Types of interaction include:

a) Interactions between organisms and their abiotic environment
Producers (*autotrophs*) such as plants have a direct interaction with their abiotic environment through the process of photosynthesis, requiring as it does solar energy and carbon dioxide from the atmosphere, and moisture and mineral nutrients from the soil. As a plant community develops on an area of bare ground, the nature of the 'soil' or edaphic environment changes as more organic material is incorporated into the soil. This is clearly illustrated in Figure 2.1.4, which shows the development of both the plant community and soil type.

Organisms at higher trophic levels, herbivores and carnivores, require reliable water supplies and are affected by extreme environmental conditions, such as drought and fire. They modify the abiotic environment through contributing to soil erosion, and by adding organic matter and nutrients from excreta. Increasing technology and an expanding population are resulting in an ever increasing impact on the abiotic environment by a variety of human activities.

b) Interactions between the various organisms in a community

Interactions may be:

1 *Interspecific*, involving interaction between *different* species, as illustrated by food chains and food webs. Competition also occurs between different plant and animal species. With plants it is competition for light, nutrients and space, and may involve the plant releasing a chemical into the soil called an *allelopath*, which inhibits the growth of other plants. Animals of different species will compete for territory. In any ecosystem, a specific species occupies a unique position within it, known as its **ecological niche**. This is also related to the concept of *resource partitioning*, where the resources of the ecosystem are shared through:

■ *Vertical separation* – i.e. the stratification of plants in a woodland, allows different animals to have a particular niche in one of the layers.
■ *Spatial (horizontal) separation* – different organisms occupy different micro-habitats.
■ *Temporal (time) separation* – some animals may be active during the day (diurnal) but others are active at night (nocturnal), and
■ *Morphological or behavioural adaptations* – such as different beak shapes on birds, which allow them to consume different foods.

2 *Intraspecific*, involving competition between individuals of the *same* species. They are illustrated by the phrase 'the survival of the fittest' as either plants compete for the available resources or animals fight for food, water, territory and a mate.

STUDENT ACTIVITY 2.7

With reference to Figure 2.2.3, analyse the different responses of the three plant types – **competitors**, **stress tolerators** and **ruderals** – to stress and disturbance.

STUDENT ACTIVITY 2.8

Refer to one of the ecosystem types in Chapters 3 to 5 and describe:
a) the interaction between its organism and their abiotic environment, and
b) the interspecific interaction within the ecosystem.

3
GLOBAL ECOSYSTEMS — FORESTS

Key Ideas

■ As a consequence of lower insolation levels and a seasonal growth pattern the productivity of temperate forests is lower than tropical rainforests.

■ Tropical rainforests are very complex ecosystems, which cover approximately 5 per cent of the Earth's surface.

■ Forests need to be managed using a sustainable approach.

■ Deforestation disrupts the normal cycling of nutrients in a forest ecosystem, affects the local climate, and also causes increased surface runoff and soil erosion.

■ In Europe, especially, the majority of temperate deciduous forests have been replaced by other land uses, particularly agriculture and urban development.

Introduction

FIGURE 3.0.1 The major biomes of the World

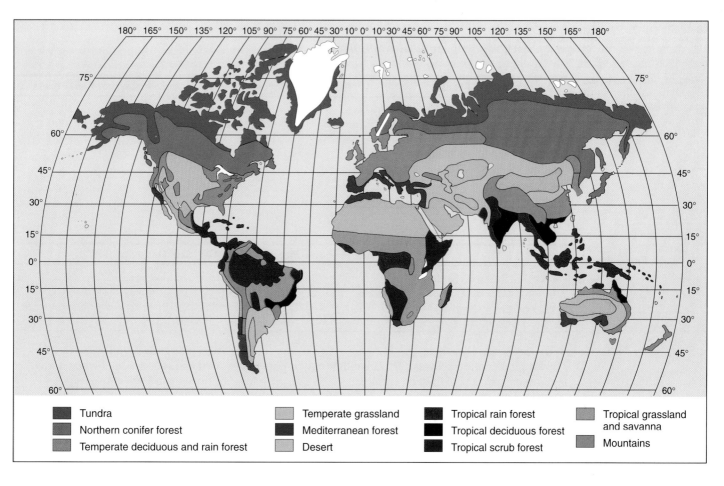

Tundra	Temperate grassland	Tropical rain forest	Tropical grassland and savanna
Northern conifer forest	Mediterranean forest	Tropical deciduous forest	Mountains
Temperate deciduous and rain forest	Desert	Tropical scrub forest	

FIGURE 3.0.2 Forest data

Change in forest area 1980–1995	Percentage	Country	Percentage of world's total forests
Europe	4.1		
N America	2.6	Russia	22.1
Australasia/Japan	1.0	Brazil	15.9
Developed World	2.7	Canada	7.1
Asia/Oceania	−6.4	US	6.2
Africa	−10.5	China	3.9
South America	−9.7	Indonesia	3.2
Developing World	−9.1	Zaire	3.1

At a global scale, the distribution of flora (plants) and fauna (animals) is very complicated, and consequently it is necessary to employ techniques which allow us to investigate these distributions at a more general level. It is possible, at a world scale, to identify floristic or phyto – geographical regions which contain similar plant species, and faunal or zoo – geographical regions containing similar animal species. These areas appear to be closely linked to specific global climatic, and (in the case of plants) soil regions, and by combining them 'natural' regions are produced. These regions are now known as biogeographical regions or **biomes**. Figure 3.0.1 illustrates the distribution of the major biome types.

Figure 3.0.2 illustrates the alarming rate at which forests in the 'Developing World' are being lost to other land uses, particularly agriculture. Many areas of the 'Developed World' have already lost the majority of their forests, and are trying to increase their forest areas through afforestation. This chapter uses a selection of case studies to analyse some of the forest-related problems that need to be managed.

3.1 Tropical Rainforests

The Distribution of Tropical Rainforests

FIGURE 3.1.1 The major countries with tropical rainforest (hectares)

American Rain Forest		African Rainforest		Indo-Malaysian Rain Forest	
Brazil	2 800 000	Zaire	1 100 000	Burma	300 000
Peru	500 000	Sudan	400 000	Malaysia	200 000
Columbia	400 000	Others	100 000	Others	400 000
Venezuela	300 000				
Guyanas	300 000				
Bolivia	160 000				
Equador	100 000				

FIGURE 3.1.2 Tropical rainforest climate

			Jan	Feb	Mar	Apl	May	June	July	Aug	Sep	Oct	Nov	Dec		
Manaus	Latitude 3S	Rainfall mm	276	277	301	287	193	99	61	41	62	112	165	228	Total mm	2102
	Altitude 60m	Temp C	26	26	26	26	26	27	27	28	28	28	27	27	Range C	2
Singapore	Latitude 1N	Rainfall mm	285	164	154	160	131	177	163	200	122	184	236	306	Total mm	2282
	Altitude 10m	Temp C	26	27	27	28	28	28	27	27	27	27	27	26	Range C	2

True tropical rainforest covers only 718 million hectares or 5 per cent of the land surface. It is, however, very difficult to obtain precise figures of the areal extent of vegetation types, as a result of factors such as differences in definition, how the data is measured and collected, and when it was collected. The three main areas of tropical rainforest, mainly located between 10 degrees north and south of the Equator, are shown in Figures 3.0.1 and 3.1.1.

The Climate and Soils of the Tropical Rainforest

The combination throughout the year of high temperatures and high precipitation totals, leads to very high levels of weathering of the underlying rocks of the rainforest, especially by chemical weathering processes. This can produce a weathered layer (the regolith) of over 30 metres.

As for most of the year precipitation exceeds evapotranspiration, there is a downward movement of water, through the soil profile, which carries with it various soil materials. This process is called translocation, and in the case of tropical rainforests, it is of a type called ferrallitisation. As the surface leaf litter decomposes, organic acids are produced, which together with other compounds are carried through the soil profile by water movement. This leaches out soluble bases such as sodium, calcium and potassium, breaks down clay materials, and removes silica. The effect is to leave behind, or concentrate in the upper or eluviated horizon, iron and aluminium oxides (sesquioxides), producing the characteristic red or yellow colour of tropical soils.

As the parent rock is weathered it is usually turned into a clay called kaolinite, which, unfortunately, has a poor nutrient retaining capacity. If deforestation does occur, because of its high clay content, in wet periods it is subject to high rates of gullying and other types of soil erosion, but high temperatures may bake the surface layer producing a very hard zone.

The tropical rainforest nutrient cycle

Although the forest produces very large amounts of leaf fall (about 10 tonnes per hectare per year in the Amazon) to become leaf litter, it is very quickly broken down and recycled by the plants. Humus recycling figures of 1 per cent per day have been recorded. Decomposition can be 30 times the rate in a temperate deciduous forest, due mainly to the large numbers of decomposer organisms, including many species of ants and termites, but particularly fungi which occur in **mycorrhizal** association with plant roots. These allow plant nutrients to move directly from decaying plant material to the plant.

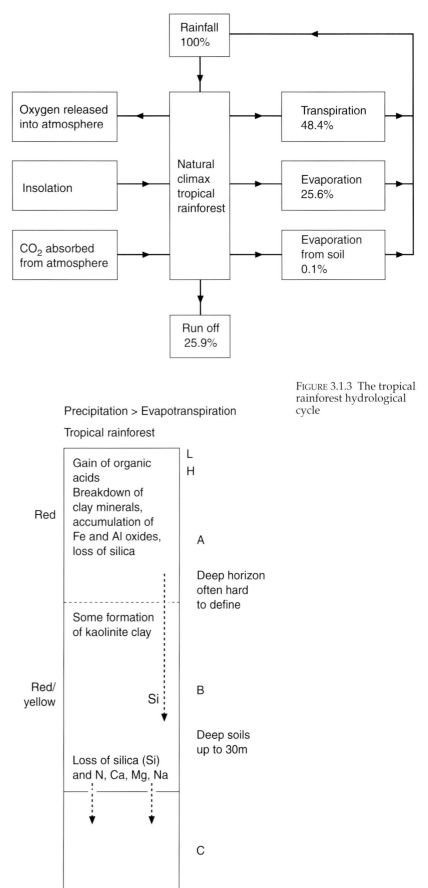

FIGURE 3.1.3 The tropical rainforest hydrological cycle

FIGURE 3.1.4 A typical tropical rainforest ferrallitic soil profile

FIGURE 3.1.5 Gersmehl's model applied to nutrient cycling in the tropical rainforest

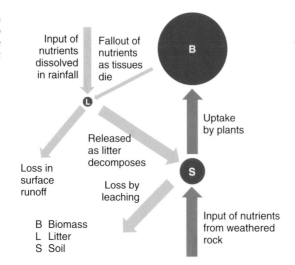

Input of nutrients dissolved in rainfall

Fallout of nutrients as tissues die

B

Uptake by plants

Released as litter decomposes

S

Loss in surface runoff

Loss by leaching

Input of nutrients from weathered rock

B Biomass
L Litter
S Soil

The size of the nutrient stores (B, L, S) is proportional to the quantity of nutrients stored. The thickness of the transfer arrows is proportional to the amount of nutrients transferred.

Plant and Animal Communities

Obviously, each area of tropical rainforest is unique but there are sufficient similarities, in the various areas, as a result of **convergent evolution** to describe a basic model.

Tropical rainforests are perhaps the most important ecosystem, containing 90 per cent (1.5 to 2 m species) of the world's biodiversity of species. In parts of the Amazonian selvas rainforest, 300 tree species have been recorded in a 2 square kilometre area, and 600 bird species and 40 000 species of insect per hectare. The reasons for this immense diversity are believed to be:

■ a long period of evolution – unlike many temperate areas tropical rainforests have been unaffected by glacial periods,
■ they are located on large continental areas with few physical barriers to the immigration of species,
■ the structure of the rainforest provides numerous ecological niches, allowing a high degree of co-existence,
■ high levels of ultra violet-B radiation, near the Equator, may have had an effect on plant and animal DNA, causing an increased level of mutations and a consequent increase in the rate of evolution of new species.

Consequently, very little humus material and few mineral nutrients are incorporated into the upper soil horizons. Most of these decomposed materials are quickly used by the large amount of plant material. This produces a closed system of mineral nutrient recycling, with most of the nutrients being stored in the biomass (Figure 3.1.5). In some areas of the Venezuelan rainforests, 60 per cent of the nitrogen, 74 per cent of the calcium, 92 per cent of the magnesium, 90 per cent of the potassium and 66 per cent of the phosphorus is located in plant material. This, clearly, has profound implications if deforestation does occur.

FIGURE 3.1.6 Relationships between tropical rainforest communities and environmental conditions

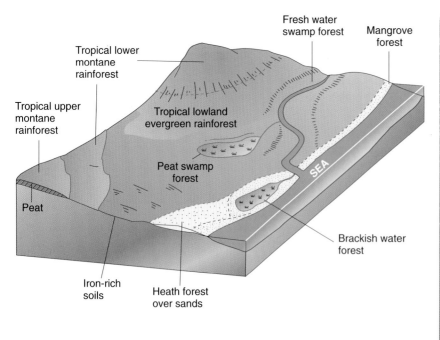

Tropical lower montane rainforest

Fresh water swamp forest

Mangrove forest

Tropical upper montane rainforest

Tropical lowland evergreen rainforest

Peat swamp forest

SEA

Peat

Brackish water forest

Iron-rich soils

Heath forest over sands

FIGURE 3.1.7 Tropical rainforest

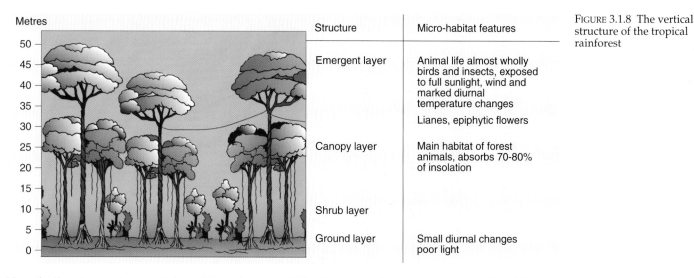

FIGURE 3.1.8 The vertical structure of the tropical rainforest

	Structure	Micro-habitat features
	Emergent layer	Animal life almost wholly birds and insects, exposed to full sunlight, wind and marked diurnal temperature changes
		Lianes, epiphytic flowers
	Canopy layer	Main habitat of forest animals, absorbs 70-80% of insolation
	Shrub layer	
	Ground layer	Small diurnal changes poor light

Near the Equator, environmental conditions for plant growth are at their optimum. Consequently, the plant productivity of the tropical rainforests is the highest of any land based ecosystem producing a mean net primary productivity figure of 2200 g/sq.m/yr (the land ecosystem average is 773).

Net primary productivity, however, varies enormously with estimates ranging from 1000 to 3500 g/sq.m/yr. The average biomass is 45 kg/cu.m compared with the land average of 12.3 kg/cu m. The world total rainforest biomass is 765 thousand m tonnes, or 42 per cent of all the living material on the continents of the Earth!

As a result of variations not only in climate, but also of soil (edaphic) conditions, relief and altitude, there is an immense variety in the type of tropical rainforest found in a particular area (Figure 3.1.6). Coastal rainforests include mangroves, which are able to survive in saline water. Where soil conditions are sandy, producing conditions of low moisture and low nutrient levels, a dwarf or 'heath' form of forest occurs. Inland, where the water table is at or very near the surface, peat swamp or freshwater swamp forest develops. The increased rainfall and lower temperatures of mountain areas produces 'montane' forest.

Structure of the Rainforest

The rainforest is dominated by a large range of tree species. Teak, mahogany and ebony are all well known valuable trees for commercial logging. As a result of 70 per cent of the trees having been felled and exported, mainly to Europe and Japan, the 'big leaf mahogany' of the Amazon is now one of the top ten most endangered species in the world.

STUDENT ACTIVITY 3.3

Study Figure 3.1.6, and analyse the variations in the types of tropical rainforest.

Other trees include crop trees such as the rubber, wild banana and cocoa. The cocoa tree is one of several which produce fruit seed pods on the trunk and branches, a habit called cauliflory. In Malaysia and Indonesia, there are a large number of species of **dipterocarps**.

As Figure 3.1.8 illustrates, the vertical structure consists of four major layers. This large number of layers produces a wide range of potential ecological niches, and **stratum specificity**, where particular combinations of plants and animals occur in a specific vertical zone. Diversity is further enhanced by the large number of nocturnal species, producing complex food webs (Figure 3.1.9). It has been estimated that in the Amazon there are 1500 species of fish, 2000 bird species, and that insects make up 80 per cent of the animal biomass, with 40 000 species of insects per hectare.

To allow them to survive in a very competitive environment, the plants of the rainforest have developed a remarkable range of adaptations:

(a) leaves – are often long lived,
    – may contain 75 per cent of the nutrients of the tree,
    – often have a thick waxy surface (epidermis or cuticle) which is resistant to insects and helps to remove rainwater,
    – have modified stomata to help reduce transpiration,
    – have a 'drip tip' shape to help to remove rainwater,
    – have mosses and lichens growing on them which help to fix and absorb nutrients,

(b) trees have buttress or surface roots to improve stability (not only as a result of their height but because many rainforest areas are hurricane or tropical storm zones),

(c) many trees have a thick bark to help protect them from insects and to conserve moisture,

(d) there are many types of climbing plants or **lianes**,

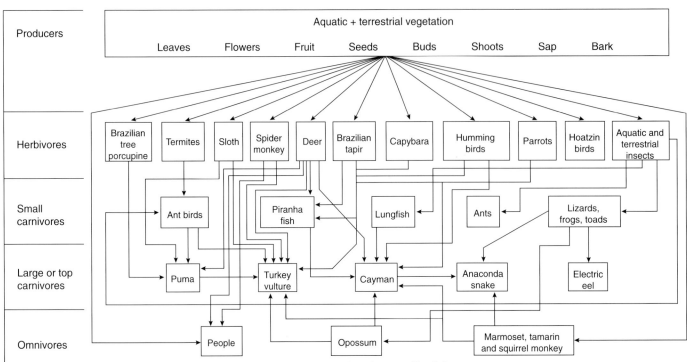

Producers	Aquatic + terrestrial vegetation
	Leaves Flowers Fruit Seeds Buds Shoots Sap Bark

Arrows show direction of energy (food) flow

FIGURE 3.1.9 A Brazilian tropical rainforest food web

(e) **epiphytes**, including orchids, live high above ground on, but not off i.e. they are not parasitic, the branches of trees, using aerial roots to absorb nutrients, and in some cases to carry out photosynthesis,

(f) stranglers are similar to epiphytes, but are parasitic as their roots eventually reach the ground, surrounding and eventually killing the host tree,

(g) **saprophytes** are fungi which do not need to carry out photosynthesis but instead live by absorbing nutrients from other plants and decaying material.

The Destruction of the Tropical Rainforest

Since 1945, an estimated 40 per cent of the world's tropical rainforest has been destroyed. As with data on the extent of the rainforest it is difficult to be precise about the actual rates of forest loss as rates vary enormously both over time and in different areas (Figures 3.1.10 and 3.1.12). The World Conservation Monitoring Centre has estimated that 16 390 000 hectares, an area the size of England and Wales, are lost every year.

The Reasons for Deforestation

Between areas there are enormous variations in the rates of deforestation, and similarly there are numerous reasons why deforestation occurs, but essentially there are two major factors to be considered:

■ increasing population pressures in an area or a country, and
■ the consequences of economic development. The following case study illustrates some of the factors behind the high rates of deforestation in Brazil.

FIGURE 3.1.10 The top 10 countries in terms of rainforest destruction

Country	Area lost each year (sq. km)	% of total forest
Brazil	34 400	0.7
Indonesia	12 150	1
Bolivia	10 120	2.1
Mexico	9300	1.9
Venezuela	8500	1.5
Zaire	7300	0.6
Peru	5700	0.9
Myanmar (Burma)	4850	1.6
Sudan	4450	1
Malaysia	3650	2

CASE STUDY

Developments in the Brazilian Amazon

Year	Population (millions)	Birth rate per 1000	Death rate per 1000	Natural increase %	Estimated population 2025	Urban %	GNP per capita $US
1994	155.3	25	8	1.7	200	76	2770
1995	157.8	25	8	1.7	225	77	3020
1996	160.5	25	8	1.7	202	76	3370
1997	160.3	27	7	2.0	213	76	3640

FIGURE 3.1.11 Population and economic data for Brazil

Brazilian Amazonia covers an area of over 5 million square kilometres, or 57 per cent of Brazil's land area. It contains only 4 per cent of the country's population, and generates only 2 per cent of the total Gross Domestic Product. Brazil is the world's eighth largest economy, and some of its population and economic details are shown in Figure 3.1.11.

FIGURE 3.1.12

> ### Brazil admits increase in burning of rainforest
>
> Destruction of the Amazonian rainforest nearly tripled between the 1990–91 and 1994–95 burning seasons, according to information issued by the Brazilian government.
> The figures show that 11,196 square miles of Amazon rainforest were destroyed in the 1994–95 burning season, an area about the size of Belgium. In contrast, on the eve of the 1992 Earth Summit in Rio, deforestation had dipped to 4,247 square miles. The figures issued on Monday show that 6,950 square miles of the Amazon were destroyed from 1995 to 1996. Earlier this month a separate study issued by a congressional commission said 22,393 square miles of the Amazon were being destroyed each year through deforestation.
> *Guardian* 28 January 1998

STUDENT ACTIVITY 3.4

1 Locate, on an outline World map, the countries shown on Figure 3.1.10 and select a suitable technique to show the area lost each year.
2 Refer to Figure 3.1.12 and describe the recent levels of deforestation in Brazil.

FIGURE 3.1.13 The Carajas project

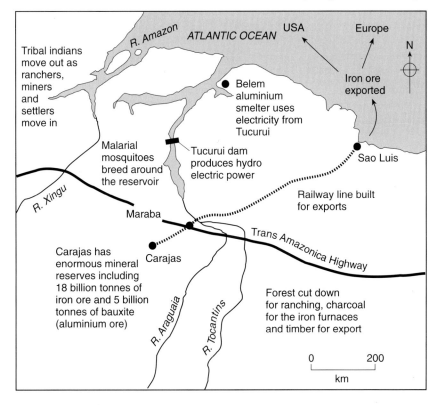

FIGURE 3.1.14 New developments in Amazonia

Proposed Scheme	Potential Impact
Paving the BR 174 and 364 roads between Brazil, Peru and Venezuela	The BR174 runs through or near the lands of 16 000 Indians and several ecological reserves. The BR364 runs through forest suitable for logging, and could also be used as a new cocaine drug route.
Dredging the Amazon River to improve navigation	Will pollute the water supplies of local communities
Dredging the Madeira River to improve navigation	Will pollute the water supplies used by five indigenous communities
Building a 2000 mile waterway network joining the Tocantins and Araguaia Rivers, to allow grain to be shipped from Belem	Involves draining numerous wetlands, including the Bananal Island National Park which has a unique biodiversity and is home to 6000 Indians
The building of the Ferronorte, a 3000 mile railway between Mato Grosso and Para States	Involves the loss of forest Will open up 800 000 square miles for farming, particularly for export crops such as soya bean leading to large scale pesticide pollution
The building of a 1000 mile electricity transmission line between the Tucurui dam and various towns in Para State	Involves the loss of forest
Building a natural gas pipeline between the Urucu field and Manaus	Involves the loss of forest

The Greater Carajas Project is one of the 15 economic growth poles created in Amazonia by the POLAMAZONIA scheme. The Project is financed by a $2 000 000 000 loan from the World Bank and the European Union, and some of its features are shown on Figure 3.1.13. The Project also involves the clearance of forest for extensive cattle ranching, but the poor nutrient status of the soil, following clearance, means that stocking levels are very low with 1500 cattle requiring 3000 hectares of grazing.

Developments such as the Greater Carajas Project have led to conflict between several organisations. The UDR, the cattle rancher's organisation are generally in favour of the government's proposals, but FUNAI the National Indian Foundation, supported by ecologists from Europe and the United States are campaigning for a more sustainable approach to development.

In August 1997 the Brazilian Government, in response to an upturn in the economy, announced seven new schemes (Figure 3.1.14) for Amazonia, costing $3 bn and due for completion by 1999. It also proposes to build an additional 10 hydro-electric power stations.

In 1998, the Brazilian Government announced the creation of a 640 km long conservation corridor along the River Amazon, 400 kilometres west of Manaus. The designation of the Amara Sustainable Development Reserve (SDR) links the existing Mamiraua SDR to the west, and the Jau National Park to the east. The 'sustainable' designation of the Amara SDR will allow its 2000 inhabitants to remain in their homes, and be actively involved in the management of the reserve, which contains many endangered species including Amazonian manatees, black caimans, river dolphins, jaguars, black uakari monkeys, and harpy eagles.

The Impact of Rainforest Destruction

At a variety of scales, from local to international, the destruction of the rainforest has an impact on both environmental and human systems (Figure 3.1.15). Locally, in the past, the indigenous native populations, for example the Kayapo in Amazonia, and the Dayaks of Malaysia have used the forest for shifting cultivation, in a largely sustainable form, by clearing and burning the forest, and then using it for several years before moving to new locations.

The increased light levels following the clearance allow the growth of a secondary type of forest, lower in height and with a reduced range of species. Increasing population trends, and a desire by many governments to see such peoples settled and integrated into the main economy, have seen the development of a form of subsistence agriculture which has a much greater impact on the forest. This may result in the total destruction of the forest and its replacement by areas under permanent cultivation.

Impact on the water cycle	■ bare soil increases surface runoff ■ increased flood risk downstream ■ rainfall reduced
Impact on soils and landforms	■ increased soil erosion as a result of sheetwash, gullying and aeolian processes ■ increased risk of landslides ■ increased sediment load in rivers ■ loss of soil nutrients ■ reduction in soil fertility ■ formation of lateritic crusts
Impact on plants and animals	■ original primary forest destroyed or replaced by inferior secondary forest ■ diversity of plant and animal species reduced ■ transpiration reduced
Impact on the climate	■ bare soil increases albedo rates ■ burning of trees increases carbon dioxide levels in the atmosphere contributing to global warming ■ diurnal range of temperature increases ■ rainfall decreases ■ less carbon dioxide absorbed and less oxygen produced
Impact on native population	■ loss of traditional way of life ■ loss of land ■ introduction of new diseases

FIGURE 3.1.15 A summary of some of the impacts of rainforest destruction

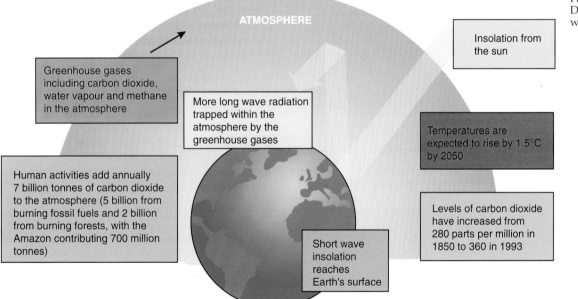

FIGURE 3.1.16 Deforestation and global warming

The felling and burning of the forests is believed to be having a major impact on the climate of the world by increasing levels of carbon dioxide in the atmosphere (Figure 3.1.16).

In September 1997, the issue of tropical rainforest destruction was brought to the attention of the world's media, when it was combined with two other environmental concerns. A major pollution incident covering large areas of south east Asia, and centred on Indonesia and Malaysia, occurred due to the burning of large areas of rainforest in Indonesia. The burning became uncontrollable, as the area was already being affected by a drought, thought to be the result of the El Nino effect in the Pacific Ocean.

The high smoke levels trapped gases, including carbon monoxide, nitrous oxide, sulphur dioxide and ozone, especially in urban areas such as Kuching and Kuala Lumpur, producing a dangerous photo-chemical smog (Figure 3.1.19).

STUDENT ACTIVITY 3.5

With reference to Figures 3.1.15 and 3.1.16, analyse the climatic effects of the destruction of the tropical rainforest.

FIGURE 3.1.17 Soil nutrient change

Land use	Soil characteristics (percentage)			
	organic content	cation exchange capacity	nitrogen	phosphorus
Natural forest	100	100	100	100
1 year after clearance (land unused)	104	82	66	120
After two years of cultivation	46	51	36	75

FIGURE 3.1.18 The Korup Project is an example of a biosphere reserve, consisting of three distinct zones, each of which has a particular function. Korup was made a National Park in 1986

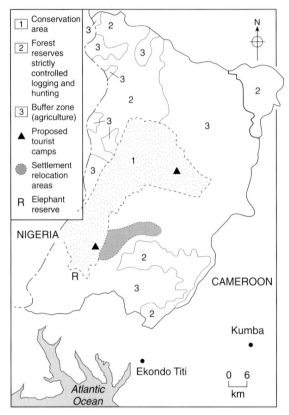

STUDENT ACTIVITY 3.6

Figure 3.1.17 illustrates the changes that would take place to selected soil characteristics, following the clearing and burning of an area of equatorial rainforest and its replacement by cultivation.
Describe and explain the changes.

The Management of the Rainforests

Obviously, there are numerous issues to be resolved in the management of the rainforests, involving the integration of a wide range of very different points of view. Some of the possible management alternatives are summarised below, and in the following case study of Malaysia.

1 The conservation of specific areas by the creation of biosphere reserves (Figure 3.1.18) involving:

■ the defining of a core area providing total conservation protection for the area,
■ the creation of buffer zone 1 where research is permitted, and
■ the creation of buffer zone 2 where tourism and native settlements are permitted.

2 The sustainable management of the forest's resources.
3 The development of rural village communities in order to reduce the pressure from the local population on the forest. This would involve developing alternatives to biomass fuel, new craft based industry, education, agro-forestry (where crops are grown alongside trees), and the introduction of plantation crops.
4 The development of eco-tourism or green tourism.
5 The introduction of the concept of 'debt for nature', where a country's foreign debt is written off in exchange for the conservation of specific areas.

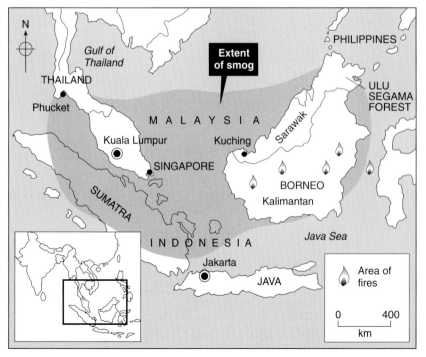

FIGURE 3.1.19 South east Asia and the forest fires of Indonesia

CASE STUDY

The rainforests of Malaysia

Year	Population (millions)	Birth rate per 1000	Death rate per 1000	Natural increase %	Estimated population 2025	Urban %	GNP per capita $US
1994	19.5	28	5	2.3	34.3	51	2790
1995	19.9	29	5	2.4	34.5	51	3160
1996	20.6	28	5	2.3	34.5	51	3560
1997	21.0	27	5	2.2	32.8	51	3890

FIGURE 3.1.20 Population and economic data for Malaysia

Date	1900	1960	1965	1970	1975	1980	1985	1990
Forested area (000's ha)	13 000	9465	8556	8009	7290	6360	6190	6150
%	99	72	65	61	55	48	47	47

FIGURE 3.1.21 Changes in the forested area of Peninsula Malaysia

Malaysia comprises peninsular Malaysia, together with Sabah and Sarawak on the former island of Borneo (Figure 3.1.19), and contains extensive areas of rainforest, with a very high biodiversity (Figure 3.1.22). In common with so many other countries, continued high rates of economic and population growth (Figure 3.1.20) are subjecting its forests to intense pressures.

Figure 3.1.21 illustrates the decline in the forested area of peninsular Malaysia between 1900 and 1990. Malaysia is, after Indonesia, the second largest tropical timber exporting country, with timber exports providing 10 per cent of its export income. The Malaysian Government appreciates that the forests:

- protect and maintain fresh water supplies,
- maintain the stability of the climate by absorbing carbon dioxide,
- enrich the soil with organic and mineral material,
- reduce the rates of soil erosion, and
- provide a wide variety of timber products.

Malaysia is aware both of the pressure on its forests, and of the need for their sustainable development, and as a result it has passed a number of laws, including the 1980 National Parks Act, and the 1984 National Forestry Act, to implement a wide variety of forest management policies. The aims of which are:

- to preserve habitats,
- to protect species,
- to carry out conservation research, and
- to manage the forests by sustainable methods.

	UK	Malaysia	DVCA
Area sq. km	244 000	332 000	
Flowering plants	1350	5500	
Trees	35	2600	1295
Ferns	80	500	
Mammals	48	203	110
Birds	210	616	275
Fishes	38	260	37
Snakes	3	141	71
Amphibians	6	93	56
Butterflies	43	1022	
Termites	0	100+	

FIGURE 3.1.22 Biodiversity in the UK, Malaysia and the DVCA

Government forest policy has included the creation of conservation areas based on the biosphere concept. These consist of:

1 The **core** conservation zones called *Virgin Jungle Reserves* – One hundred and twenty of these reserves, for example the Danum Valley Conservation Area (DVCA) have been created, covering 111 700 hectares. Policies in these areas include a captive breeding programme, which has allowed endangered species, such as orang-utan, gibbons, Asian elephants and rhinoceros, to be returned to the forests, together with the establishment of gene banks and seed orchards.

2 The **buffer zone** areas formed by the *Permanent Forest Reserves* – Reserves such as the Ulu Segama Forest Reserve (USFR) have been created (covering 43 per cent of the country), around the Virgin Jungle Reserves such as the DVCA. Within these reserves are the *Production Forests*, where commercial timber is extracted using a renewable cycle of between 25 and 60 years. Before felling takes place a forest inventory is taken, and there is then the enforcement of a minimum size standard (trees must have a diameter of at least 45 centimetres) in order to be harvested. A selective management policy is also used, in involving at least 32 trees,

---

STUDENT ACTIVITY 3.7

With reference to the case study of Malaysia, and any other available information, evaluate the options available for the management of the tropical rainforests.

FIGURE 3.1.23

Effect of Logging on Soils			Forest suspended sediment (mg/l)		
	Forest soil	**Lumbered soil**	**Storm**	**Undisturbed**	**Logged**
Bulk density (g/cu.m)	0.52	1.44	1	2613	5734
Moisture content (%)	28.8	19.7	2	484	2454
Organic carbon (%)	2.7	1.27	3	1885	3338
Total N (%)	0.23	0.07	4	1524	5486
Total P (%)	177.8	123.2	Average	1627	4253
Soluble P (mg/kg)	2.27	1.01			
pH	4.7	5			

each hectare, of 30 centimetres diameter or more, being retained after harvesting. These may then be harvested in the next 25–60 year cycle. In addition, directional felling is practiced to reduce environmental damage.

Other projects have included the:

1 *Compensatory Forest Plantation Project* – This project began in 1982, and involves logged over forests. After harvesting, they are replanted with fast growing species such as *Acacia mangium*, *Gmelina arborea* and *Paraserianthese falcataria*, which allow harvesting after only 15 years. Clearly, this type of planting of secondary forest is no substitute for the original primary forest.

2 *Permanent Settlement Policy* – The government is also trying to resolve the problem of shifting cultivation by encouraging the indigenous population to settle on permanent sites. In order to achieve this they have a programme of soil enrichment and afforestation. In Sabah and Sarawak, peoples such as the Dayaks and Penan are in conflict with the government over this policy, and the loss of access to areas of forest, which are due to be logged.

STUDENT ACTIVITY 3.8

Assume the role of a soil scientist, who has been asked to prepare a report on *'The implications of logging on the soils and hydrology of a tropical rain forest catchment area'*.
Using Figure 3.1.23 and any other information:
1 Analyse the effects of logging, on forest soils and river hydrology.
2 Explain how these effects can be managed in order to reduce their impacts.

3.2 Temperate Forests

Temperate forests, particularly those in Europe, have been severely reduced in area. Many forests near to industrial regions are being affected by acid rain, and concern is being expressed about the 'clear-fell' lumbering techniques used by some timber companies.

Sclerophyllous (Mediterranean) forest ecosystems – climate and soils

Soils in these areas are transitional between the brown earths of temperate deciduous forest regions and the red and grey soils of tropical deserts. The highly seasonal nature of the rainfall results in contrasting processes in winter and summer.

During the winter, the higher rainfall totals produce a downward movement of clay (eluviation) and iron through the soil profile. In summer, the high levels of evaporation and transpiration may cause calcium to move upwards and to be precipitated in the B horizon. The combination of these processes may produce a **brown Mediterranean** soil (Figure 3.2.2). In many of the limestone areas a **red Mediterranean** or **terra rossa** soil may form in the eroded remains of brown Mediterranean soils. Where the dry season increases, that is nearer the desert margins, a **cinnamon** soil may form.

FIGURE 3.2.1
Mediterranean climates

			Jan	Feb	Mar	Apl	May	June	July	Aug	Sep	Oct	Nov	Dec		
Palermo	Latitude 38 N	Rainfall mm	127	91	66	43	20	5	3	43	30	94	99	89	Total mm	710
	Altitude 108 m	Temp C	11	12	13	16	22	23	26	26	24	20	16	13	Range C	15
Perth	Latitude 32 S	Rainfall mm	8	10	20	43	130	180	170	149	86	56	20	13	Total mm	881
	Altitude 60 m	Temp C	23	23	22	19	16	14	13	13	15	16	19	22	Range C	10

Winter precipitation > evapotranspiration
Summer evapotranspiration > precipitation

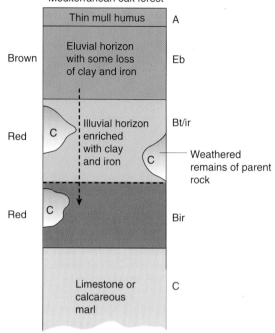

Mediterranean oak forest

Brown Mediterranean soil

FIGURE 3.2.2 A brown
Mediterranean Soil
Profile

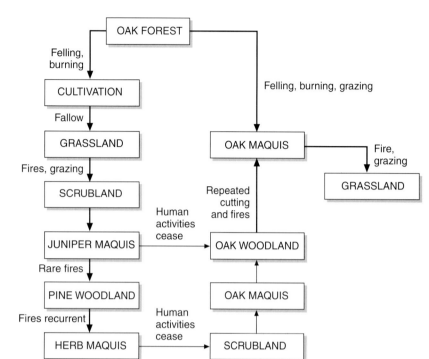

FIGURE 3.2.3 Human
activities and vegetation
change on limestone
uplands in
Mediterranean areas

Plants and animals

In most 'Mediterranean type' ecosystems, very few areas of original vegetation have survived the effects of human activities, such as forestry, agriculture, and urban growth. Most vegetated areas are now covered by a secondary succession of **sclerophyllous**, usually scrub, vegetation. This type of vegetation is xerophytic, and has adaptations to reduce moisture loss. These include hardened waxy cuticularised leaves (sclerophyllous), protected stomata, and reduced leaf size (microphyllous). Along the northern coast of the Mediterranean Sea it is believed that the 'original' primary vegetation was evergreen forest as small areas have survived. These forests consist of evergreen oaks (for example, cork oak, holm oak), together with various pines, including parasol pine, maritime pine, Aleppo pine, and firs, cypresses and cedars.

Throughout most of the Mediterranean region the present vegetation consists of degraded scrub called either *maquis* or *garrigue* (Figure 3.2.3).

Maquis scrub vegetation consists of woody, low-growing (less than 3 metres) shrubs, including wild olive, carob, arbutus or strawberry tree, myrtle, juniper, yew, heathers, gorse, and brooms. The garrigue is usually found on limestone rocks, where conditions are more extreme, with higher temperatures and little available moisture. The plants are similar to those in the maquis areas, but are dwarf forms and are more widely spaced.

In central California, similar shrub vegetation occurs and is known as *chaparral*. Species include the dwarf oak, which is deciduous and under 3

metres in height, bush oaks, chamiso bush, manzanita, wild cherry, buckthorns, and in the wetter areas, evergreen oaks and pinon pines. This area of California has over 200 species of vertebrates, 75 per cent of them being bird species. The mammals include ground squirrels, wood rat, mule deer, and in some of the wilderness areas, mountain lion and grizzly bear. Central Chile has a community consisting of evergreen beech, sumac, Chile soaptree, Chile gumbox, southern cypress, and Araucarian pines. The Cape Province of South Africa has a very varied flora, with similar species to those in Chile.

The net primary productivity (NPP) of these areas, on average, is quite low at 700 g/sq.m/yr, reflecting the constraints imposed by the long summer drought. Fire is an important factor in the development of vegetation in these areas. Many plants are *pyrophytes*, with special adaptations to withstand the effects of burning. Fire may stimulate the germination of some types of seed, species such as the Eucalyptus produce numerous stems from the burnt stumps, and many plants have thickened bark. Fire destroys *phytotoxic* substances, which are poisonous to some plants, bacteria and soil organisms.

STUDENT ACTIVITY 3.9

With reference to Figures 3.2.1 and 3.2.3 assess the extent that climatic and soil conditions have influenced the type of vegetation in Mediterranean areas.

CASE STUDY

South western Australia

The south western area of Australia, centred around Perth has a Mediterranean type climate, and a unique variety of habitats (Figure 3.2.4). These are closely related to changes in climate and soil type. As the precipitation decreases from over 750 mm in the west to below 250 mm in the east on the Darling Plain, the vegetation changes from sclerophyllous forest on podzolic soils (in the Perth area), to temperate woodland and mallee on red-brown earths (chestnut soils) around Narrogin. This in turn is replaced in the Merredin area by a complex mosaic of temperate woodland, semi-arid mallee and heath.

The sclerophyllous forest is a continuous canopy of sclerophyllous evergreen trees, including Eucalyptus species, cypress pines, and Acacia species. The Eucalyptus species include many types of hardwoods, including jarrah, karri, and marri. In the extreme south west, where the climate is wetter and the soils are more fertile, the karri forests contain trees which can reach 80 m in height. Temperate woodland is similar, but more open, and with smaller trees and more shrub forms. Mallee is a mixture of a shrub form of Eucalyptus, between 3 to 6 metres high, grasses including spinifex (porcupine grass), and herbs.

Much of the original primary forest has been replaced by secondary forest, or has been felled and cleared, to allow agriculture and urbanisation to take place. Since 1829, it has been estimated that 2.6 m hectares, or 50 per cent, of the original forest has been lost, and if present rates of loss continue all primary forest will be lost by 2030.

In Western Australia the state government controls 2.1 million hectares of primary forest, managed by the Department of Conservation and Land Management (CALM). Of that total only 480 000 hectares (23 per cent) is unlogged. Local conservationists have expressed considerable concern at the rate of logging. In 1994, an article in 'The Real Forest News' (published by the Western Australian Forest Alliance), reported that, in March 1994, the Australian Heritage Committee (AHC), had included 40 areas of Western Australia's primary forest, on the interim list of the Registers of the National Estate. This is the highest national recognition of the ecological value of an area, and requires that the Federal Minister for the Environment is legally bound to prevent logging in these areas. CALM, however, planned to clear-fell many such listed areas to produce woodchip mainly for export to Japan. Clear-felling involves the total clearance of an area of forest, varying in size from 200 hectares in karri forests to 800 hectares in the jarrah-marri forests. After felling has taken place, the area is burned and then replanted, usually with quick growing karri seedlings.

Of the 480 000 hectares of presently unlogged state owned forest, only 160 000 hectares (approximately 33 per cent) are in conservation reserves. The destruction of the primary forests in western Australia has produced several major environmental effects:

1 The destruction of natural habitats has reduced the biodiversity of the area. Rare species including the chuditch (a native cat), the Western ringtailed possum, the whipbird, and the water rat have been particularly affected.
2 The lack of vegetation cover in some areas has increased surface run off, causing the rates of soil erosion to increase, resulting in increased sediment loads in local rivers.
3 As the forest cover has been removed, transpiration rates have reduced, allowing the water table to rise, enabling capillarity to bring salts to the surface, resulting in the salinisation of soils.

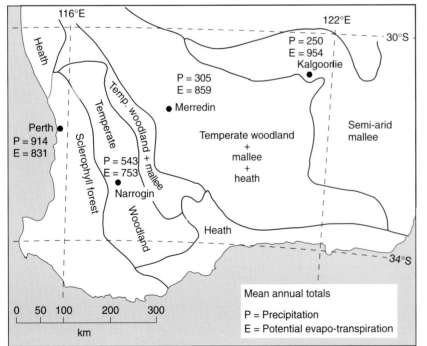

FIGURE 3.2.4 Vegetation zones in South western Australia

STUDENT ACTIVITY 3.10

Why is it important that the forests of south western Australia should be managed through the application of ecological knowledge and concepts?

Temperate deciduous forest ecosystems – climate and soils

			Jan	Feb	Mar	Apl	May	June	July	Aug	Sep	Oct	Nov	Dec	
Brest	Latitude 48 N	Rainfall mm	89	76	64	64	48	51	51	56	58	91	107	112	Total 867 mm
	Altitude 17 m	Temp C	7	7	8	10	13	16	17	18	16	13	9	8	Range 11 C
Invercargill (New Zealand)	Latitude 46 S	Rainfall mm	107	84	102	104	112	91	81	81	81	104	106	102	Total 1155 mm
	Altitude 4 m	Temp C	14	14	13	11	7	6	5	7	8	11	11	13	Range 9 C
Raleigh (USA)	Latitude 36 N	Rainfall mm	83	83	91	88	86	103	139	126	114	72	74	83	Total 1142 mm
	Altitude 140 m	Temp C	5	6	10	15	19	24	26	25	23	16	10	6	Range 21 C

FIGURE 3.2.5 The climate of temperate deciduous forests

The typical zonal soil of temperate deciduous forests is the **brown earth** (Figure 3.2.6). As the precipitation of these areas averages approximately 750 mm per year, and exceeds the annual evapotranspiration total, there is usually a downward movement of soil moisture leading to leaching, but not podzolization. The leaf litter produced by the decay of the fallen leaves is not as acidic as that under coniferous trees, and this produces mull humus with a pH of 5.5 to 6.5. The increased soil fauna, especially earthworms, in the upper horizon quickly incorporate the mull humus formed into the distinctive brown coloured A horizon, which can be of considerable depths.

Calcium, magnesium and other bases are leached down through the soil profile, together with some clay (eluviation), and iron and aluminium oxides (sesquioxides), from the eluviated E horizon, which are then deposited in the darker brown coloured illuvial B horizon. Wetter conditions produce a more acidic type of humus and more leaching forming an acid brown earth.

Plants and animals

Temperate deciduous forests, composed of deciduous trees which lose their leaves in winter, are mainly confined to the Northern Hemisphere, as in the Southern Hemisphere similar latitudes have broad-leaf evergreen forests. The deciduous habit is a form of 'dormancy' in response to the seasonal climate, where the low winter temperatures make soil water unavailable, and the low energy levels limit photosynthesis. As growth is restricted to the warmer spring and summer months, the annual NPP of 1200 g/sq.m/yr is surprisingly high. Temperate deciduous or broad-leaf forests usually have a definite vertical structure consisting of four layers:

1 The *canopy layer* is formed by the dominant trees, which may reach 50 metres in height, of a limited number of species. In Europe it is rare to find more than 8 different species of trees, such as oak, beech, ash, elm and lime, per hectare. In North America there is a wider range of species, often up to 40 species per hectare, including maples, hickory, chestnuts and sweetgum.
2 The *shrub layer* may reach 15 metres, and is composed of shrubs such as birch, hazel, hawthorn and holly.

Precipitation > Evapotranspiration
Deciduous woodland

	Mull humus	L
Brown	Organic acids	A
Grey/ brown	Leaching and loss of clay particles, accumulation of organic matter Ca, Mg, Na, K	Eb
Red/ brown	Accumulation of clay, some iron, some readsorption of bases	Bt
	Some loss of Ca, Mg, Na, K	
	Weathered parent material	C

FIGURE 3.2.6 Brown forest earth soil

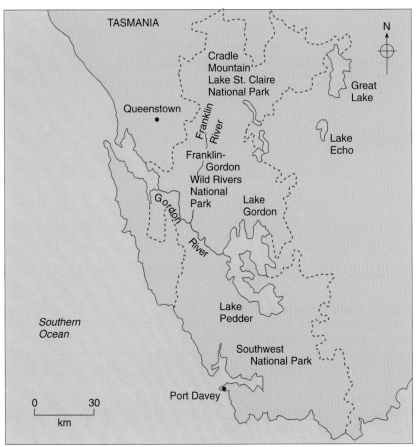

TASMANIA

Cradle
Mountain
Lake St. Claire
National Park

Great
Lake

N

Queenstown

Franklin River

Lake
Echo

Franklin-
Gordon
Wild Rivers
National
Park

Gordon

River

Lake
Gordon

Southern
Ocean

Lake
Pedder

Southwest
National Park

Port Davey

0   30
km

FIGURE 3.2.7 The
Tasmanian Wilderness
World Heritage Area

3 The *herb* or *field layer* vegetation is related to light levels. In spring, before the leaf canopy has developed, light demanding plants, *heliophytes*, including bluebells, primrose and wood anemone grow, to be replaced later by shade tolerant plants, *sciophytes*, such as dog's mercury, and ferns.
4 The *ground layer* is composed of mosses, and lichens.

The annual leaf fall is quickly broken down by such decomposers as bacteria, fungi, woodlice, earthworms and millipedes, to produce a very fertile leaf litter which is quickly incorporated into the upper soil horizon. The seasonal plant growth pattern is mirrored by some of the animals. Many birds, including the warblers and fly catchers, migrate from the woodlands in winter, while other animals, such as the black bear, squirrels, and hedgehogs hibernate.

STUDENT ACTIVITY 3.11

1 Outline how human activities have affected the Tasmanian Wilderness World Heritage Area over the past 30 years.
2 Evaluate the concept of the Recreational Opportunities Spectrum as a management technique.

CASE STUDY

Tasmanian Wilderness World Heritage Area

Tasmania is one of the few areas in the world with examples of Southern Hemisphere temperate evergreen rainforests. This type of ecosystem occurs on the western side of land masses where annual precipitation exceeds 1250 mm, and there is no dry season. It consists of a closed canopy of southern beeches with Podocarp conifers, beneath which is a shrub layer of tree ferns, lianas and nikau palms. The ground surface is covered by a tangle of slowly decomposing fallen trees, covered in mosses, fungi, ferns, and liverworts.

The south west of Tasmania has a variety of land uses, including lumbering, hydroelectric power production, mining, recreation, and sheep farming. Inevitably these uses have at times conflicted with the conservation aims of the national and state parks and, since 1982, the Tasmanian Wilderness World Heritage Area (TWWHA).

The TWWHA was designated in 1982 by the International Union for the Conservation of Nature (IUCN). It covers an area of 1.38 million hectares or 20 per cent of Tasmania (Figure 3.2.7), and has been created by the amalgamation of several national and state parks, and all but 300 hectares are owned by the Tasmanian State Government. It is a unique area containing glacial landscapes and 25 per cent of Tasmania's primary temperate rainforest.

Two-thirds of Tasmania's 32 mammal species are found in the TWWHA, together with 185 plant species endemic to Tasmania (20 per cent of which are unique to the south west of the island). Before the creation of the TWWHA, one conflict which became an international ecological issue centred on a plan by the Tasmanian Hydro Electric Commission (THEC) to dam three rivers, the Lower Gordon, the Franklin, and the King. The three rivers were located in an area which in 1981 was to be designated the Wild Rivers National Park. In 1981, construction of the dam on the River Gordon commenced, and prompted strong opposition from local groups such as the Tasmanian Wilderness Society, as well as well known environmentalists including David Bellamy. In one incident the site was blockaded and 1400 protesters were arrested. In 1983, the conflict became an important issue in the General Election campaign, with the Labour Party committed, if elected, to stopping the dam. Labour went on to win the election, and work on the dam site ceased after the government passed legislation forbidding the construction of hydro-electric plants in the TWWHA. The government paid the Tasmanian State Government $276 million in compensation.

More recently it is the impact of recreational activities which are causing concern. The TWWHA is a popular tourist destination with 597 000 visitors in 1990. In the same year, the Great Barrier Reef WHA received 2 500 000 visitors. In the TWWHA, the most popular area is Cradle Mountain–Lake St. Clair with 308 000 visitors. The TWWHA is a wilderness area, and it is important that the character of the area is maintained, but also that people are allowed to visit and appreciate its landscape and wildlife. In 1992, a management plan was introduced which zoned the TWWHA with regard to the type of recreational experience that was required by the visitors, a concept known as the Recreational Opportunities Spectrum (ROS). Four zones have been recognised:

1 The wilderness zone covering 70 per cent of the TWWHA. Here recreational activities are infrequent and involve small numbers. The natural ecosystems should be left intact to allow scientific research.
2 The self-reliant recreation zone permits informal 'expedition type' recreational activities.
3 The recreation zone where activities are more formal and organised.
4 The visitor services zones are high intensity recreational areas, located near to the main access roads, and provide a wide range of facilities.

Temperate coniferous (Taiga or Boreal) forest ecosystems – climate and soils

			Jan	Feb	Mar	Apl	May	June	July	Aug	Sep	Oct	Nov	Dec	
Yellowknife (Canada)	Latitude 62 N	Rainfall mm	13	13	10	10	15	18	28	25	23	25	18	15	Total 213 mm
	Altitude 202 m	Temp C	−28	−26	−18	−8	4	11	16	14	7	−1	−14	−25	Range 44 C
Tomsk (Russia)	Latitude 56 N	Rainfall mm	28	18	20	23	41	69	66	66	41	51	46	38	Total 507 mm
	Altitude 123 m	Temp C	−21	−18	−11	−2	7	14	17	15	14	0	−12	−19	Range 38 C

FIGURE 3.2.8 Cold temperate (Taiga or Boreal) climate

The characteristic soil of coniferous forests is the **podsol** (Figure 3.2.9). As precipitation exceeds evapo-transpiration the dominant movement of water is down through the soil profile. Due to the low temperatures, and the nature of the organic material, the rate of decomposition is slow, and pine needles, and other organic material, accumulate on the ground surface. Eventually, this produces an acidic or mor humus layer. The organic acids and chelating compounds produced by decomposition move down through the soil profile, taking with them iron and aluminium oxides (sesquioxides), a process called podsolisation. This produces an eluviated A horizon (Ea), low in iron and aluminium, but high in silica. The iron and aluminium oxides are often deposited further down the profile in the B illuviated horizon. This may lead to the formation of a narrow iron rich layer called an iron pan (Bfe). Humus may also move down, and be deposited above the iron pan (Bh). The formation of the iron pan may impede drainage down through the soil profile, leading to the formation of a waterlogged layer, a surface water gley, above the iron pan. The lack of oxygen, or anaerobic conditions, in a waterlogged soil, with the consequent slow rates of decomposition, allows the accumulation of organic material, which may eventually produce peat. Beneath the iron pan,

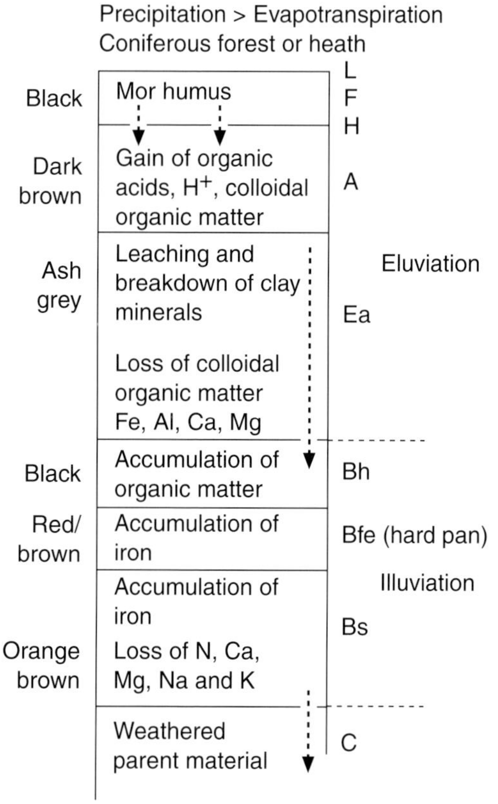

FIGURE 3.2.9 Podsol soil of coniferous forests

Precipitation > Evapotranspiration
Coniferous forest or heath

Black	Mor humus	L F H
Dark brown	Gain of organic acids, H+, colloidal organic matter	A
Ash grey	Leaching and breakdown of clay minerals	Eluviation Ea
	Loss of colloidal organic matter Fe, Al, Ca, Mg	
Black	Accumulation of organic matter	Bh
Red/ brown	Accumulation of iron	Bfe (hard pan)
	Accumulation of iron	Illuviation Bs
Orange brown	Loss of N, Ca, Mg, Na and K	
	Weathered parent material	C

some iron and aluminium oxides are deposited creating the Bs horizon. The very low winter temperatures often result in parts of the soil showing evidence of frost heaving or cryoturbation. Many coniferous forests, especially in the north of Canada and Siberia, are on permafrost.

Plants and animals

The temperate coniferous forests of the Northern Hemisphere have a fairly distinctive northern limit, the tree line, identified by an **ecotone** between coniferous forest and tundra plant communities. The forests occur where the growing season is over 3 months, and the mean daily temperature, in the warmest month, is above 10°C. The southern boundary is more variable and is an ecotone between either temperate grasslands or temperate deciduous forests.

Coniferous (evergreen) softwoods are the dominant trees, with only one or two species dominating large areas. The principal species include spruces (*Picea*), pines (*Pinus*), and firs (*Abies*), but the variety of species does vary. In Eurasia there are fewer species, mainly Scots pine and spruces, west of the Urals, than to the east where there is a variety of spruces, pines, firs, and larches. In those parts of Siberia with the lowest temperatures, conifers are replaced by deciduous

dwarf species of birch and larch. In eastern Canada, on the better drained soils, balsa fir and white spruce occur, with jack pine, black spruce and tamarack on poorly drained soils. Coniferous trees can grow up to 40 metres, and the dense canopy produced, limits the amount of light which is able to reach the ground. Consequently, ground vegetation is often very restricted. In drier areas it may be mosses and lichens, with low shrubs such as heathers occurring in slightly wetter areas. Bogs are common along flood plains and in depressions. Sphagnum mosses, sedges, and cotton grass occupy the many waterlogged depressions or 'muskegs', and the slow rate of decomposition in them leads to the development of deep peat deposits.

Coniferous trees are adapted for survival in difficult conditions. They are able, if moisture is available, to photosynthesise throughout the year. Their needle shaped leaves help to reduce transpiration, and the conical shape of the trees enables snow to fall off the trees before the branches are damaged, and to minimise wind rock. The thick bark protects the tree from both the very low winter temperatures, as well as fires, which are a common threat in summer. The average NPP of 800 g/sq.m/yr, in view of the climatic conditions, is surprisingly high. It reflects the size of the dominant trees and their ability to maintain photosynthesis even in unfavourable conditions. Annual organic litter is approximately 1 to 2 per cent of the above ground biomass. The pine needles, and other organic matter produced, decompose very slowly, allowing considerable amounts of litter to accumulate. In some areas it may amount to 100 to 500 kg/ha and represent 10 years accumulation. The litter is very acidic, and the organic acids produced (chelates) enable the process of podsolisation to occur in the soil profile.

Some of the animals in the coniferous forests are migrants. Caribou herds migrate south in winter, into the forests, from the even more extreme tundra areas. Other animals range from small rodents, to lynx, wolverine, wolves, deer, owls, hawks, grizzly and brown bears, moose and beavers.

FIGURE 3.2.10 Food web of coniferous forest

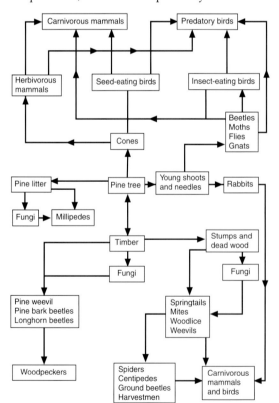

STUDENT ACTIVITY 3.12

Refer to Figure 3.1.5, which shows Gersmehl's model of nutrient flow applied to the Equatorial rainforest.
1 Use the data in Figure 3.2.11 to draw a similar graph for coniferous forest.
2 Analyse the differences in the nutrient cycles of the two ecosystems.

FIGURE 3.2.11 Nutrient cycles in Equatorial rainforests and temperate coniferous forests

Ecosystem	Nutrient storage (kg/ha)			Annual nutrient transfer	
	Biomass	**Litter**	**Soil**	**Soil to biomass**	**Biomass to litter**
Equatorial rainforest	11 081	178	352	2028	1,540
Coniferous forest	3350	2100	142	178	145

CASE STUDY

Coniferous Forests and Acid Rain

Over the past 30 years many forests in Europe and North America have experienced above average rates of dieback, where the needles or leaves of the trees discolour to yellow or red, or in extreme cases the trees actually die. In North America there has been a decline of the red spruce (*Picea rubens*), several species of southern pines (*Pinus taeda*, *P. elliottii* and *P. echinata*) and the deciduous sugar maple (*Acer saccharum*).

Rain water 'normally' has a pH of 5.6, that is, it is slightly acidic, as carbon dioxide mixes with water in the atmosphere. After World War II, increasing levels of industrialisation, increasing demands for electricity, higher car and road freight use, and the switch from coal to oil and natural gas, as the major energy sources, all contributed to higher emissions of sulphur dioxide, nitrogen dioxide, and nitrous oxide. Total annual world emissions of sulphur, related to human activities, are estimated at 70 000 000 tonnes. Other sources include volcanic eruptions. Mount Pinatubo, in 1991, released 30 m tonnes. In the UK, in 1990, 72 per cent (2 700 000 tonnes) of the sulphur dioxide came from power stations, and 51 per cent (1 400 000) of nitrogen oxides came from road transport. These gases are converted, in the atmosphere, into sulphuric and nitric acids, which may then fall as acid rain or acid deposition. Acid deposition may be either dry deposition, when the acidic products are in a gaseous or particle form, or as wet deposition from rain, snow, mist or fog. In the UK, the lowest pH, of 2.4, similar to vinegar, was recorded at Pitlochry, but West Virginia in the US has recorded 2.1. Unfortunately, acid rain is often 'exported' to other countries. A report by the National Environment Protection Board (NEPB), stated that 92 per cent of Norway's sulphur deposition came from outside its borders, mainly from the UK. The UK, however, only received 20 per cent from other countries. The problem of the long distance transfer of acid rain is partly due to attempts to control local pollution around sources such as power stations by constructing increasingly taller chimney stacks. Drax coal burning power station, in Yorkshire, which is capable of producing 10 per cent of the electricity of England and Wales, emitted 236 500 tonnes of sulphur in 1991, from a stack 259 m in height.

Germany has been particularly affected with, in 1985, 55 per cent of trees showing some sign of damage. Initially it was the silver or white fir (*Abies alba*) which was affected, but then the damage spread to Norway spruce (*Picea abies*), Scots pine (*Pinus sylvestris*), European larch (*Larix decidua*), and several broad leaved (deciduous) species, especially the European beech (*Fagus sylvatica*). A variety of reasons have been put forward to explain these declines, including climatic cycles, natural succession, extremes of weather, attacks by insects and pathogens, and natural and human disturbances. What all the affected areas have in common is the time of the decline, and this has led many ecologists to place the blame on acid rain. Germany has reduced its emissions of sulphur by implementing the international legislation shown in Figure 3.2.15. In 1994, at the Oslo conference, Germany agreed, by 2000, to reduce its sulphur emissions by 83 per cent from the 1980 level. It also spent £250 m, between 1984 and 1994, to stabilise the damaged forest areas. A report in 1995 stated

FIGURE 3.2.12 Causes and effects of acid rain

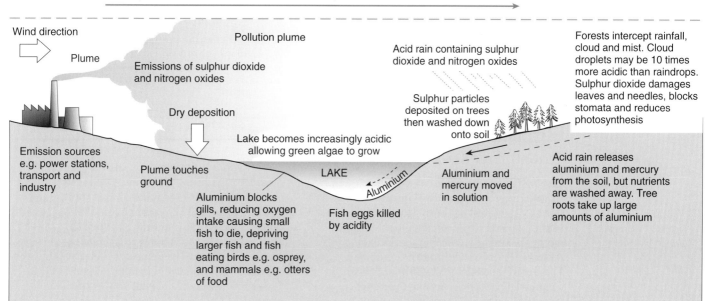

Dispersion of oxides and acids over hundreds, and even thousands of kilometres

Wind direction

Plume

Pollution plume

Emissions of sulphur dioxide and nitrogen oxides

Acid rain containing sulphur dioxide and nitrogen oxides

Dry deposition

Sulphur particles deposited on trees then washed down onto soil

Forests intercept rainfall, cloud and mist. Cloud droplets may be 10 times more acidic than raindrops. Sulphur dioxide damages leaves and needles, blocks stomata and reduces photosynthesis

Lake becomes increasingly acidic allowing green algae to grow

Emission sources e.g. power stations, transport and industry

Plume touches ground

LAKE

Aluminium

Aluminium and mercury moved in solution

Acid rain releases aluminium and mercury from the soil, but nutrients are washed away. Tree roots take up large amounts of aluminium

Aluminium blocks gills, reducing oxygen intake causing small fish to die, depriving larger fish and fish eating birds e.g. osprey, and mammals e.g. otters of food

Fish eggs killed by acidity

FIGURE 3.2.13 The effects of acid rain on soils and coniferous trees

On soils	On coniferous trees
■ A reduction in essential nutrients (e.g. Ca and Mg) due to increased leaching ■ Increased mobilisation of toxic heavy metals e.g. aluminium, which reduces bacterial activity ■ Decreased rate of organic decomposition	■ Damage to fine root hairs resulting in reduced intake of moisture and nutrients ■ Crown dieback ■ Abnormal tissue growth ■ Yellow or red needles ■ Shedding of needles ■ Failure of seedlings ■ Less resistance to frost, drought or disease

FIGURE 3.2.14 Effects of acid rain on coniferous trees

that the percentage of damaged trees, those which had lost more than 25 per cent of their needles or leaves, had dropped to 22. However, the composition of the forests has also changed. Initially they were dominated by firs, but now spruces are as common.

Action to remedy the problems caused by acid rain mainly consists of adding lime to acidified soils, lakes and rivers. In Sweden, between 1985 and 1994, the government spent £50 m liming 7100 out of 13 000 lakes affected by acidification (defined by having a pH lower than 6.0). Very little, however, can be done to improve damaged trees. The problem of acid rain has to be managed by reducing the emission of the main gases at their sources.

Year	Meeting or legislation
1979	United Nations Convention on Long Range Transboundary Air Pollution (UNCLRTAP) at Geneva
1982	Stockholm Conference on the Acidification of the Environment
1985	First Sulphur Protocol drawn up at Helsinki by UNCLRTAP, 21 countries signed (but not the UK) an agreement to limit emissions to 30 per cent by 1993
1988	EC Large Combustion Plant Directive (LCPD), UK and other EC countries agreed staged reductions of both sulphur (20% by 1993, 40% by 1998, and 60% by 2003) and nitrogen dioxide (40% by 1998)
1994	Second Sulphur Protocol drawn up at Oslo by UNCLRTAP, emissions negotiated country by country, UK agrees to an 80% reduction on 1980 figure by 2010

FIGURE 3.2.15 International action on acid rain

This is being achieved through international legislation, reducing the consumption of fossil fuels, and by using technology such as Flue Gas Desulphurisation (FGD).

STUDENT ACTIVITY 3.13

1 Explain the causes of acid rain.
2 Why is it called a trans-frontier problem, and why does this make it a difficult problem to manage?

STUDENT ACTIVITY 3.14

Why is lumbering posing a problem in British Columbia?

CASE STUDY

The Great Bear Rainforest

Originally, the temperate coastal rainforest of North America stretched from California to Alaska. Two-thirds of the forest has been removed in the past 25 years, and today, it is confined to the coastal mountain ranges of Washington, Oregon and Alaska in the USA, and British Columbia in Canada. The Great Bear Rainforest (GBR) of British Columbia (BC) represents one-quarter of the remaining rainforest, and contains some trees which are over 1000 years old. It contains over two-thirds of Canada's plant and land mammal species, and is one of the last and largest habitats of the endangered North American grizzly bear. Prince Royal Island is home to the rare white 'spirit' black bear. The Raincoast Conservation Society have estimated that there are only 1000 to 2000 grizzlies left in a habitat which should have 6000.

British Columbia once had 353 forested valleys, which descended to the Pacific Ocean. In 1998, only 69 remained intact, with 10 due to be logged in the next two years, and most of the rest over the next decade. Over 90 per cent of the forests are owned by the province of BC, which has the authority to grant licences to the forestry companies. Three companies, Western Forest Products, International Forest Products, and MacMillan Bloedel dominate the industry. The forest provides coniferous softwood from Canadian Hemlock, Douglas Fir, Western Red Cedar, and Sitka Spruce. Some of the trees are up to 90 metres in height with each one valued at £20 000. Ninety per cent of the timber produced is exported, mainly to Europe, Japan, and the US.

Greenpeace is in conflict with the forestry companies over both the extent of their operations, and their cutting methods, which often involve 'clear felling' i.e. the total destruction of parts of the forest.

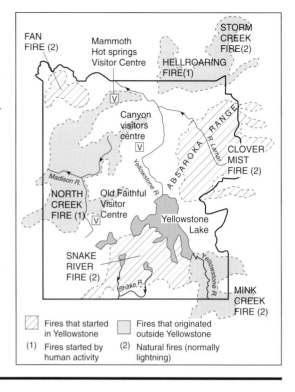

FIGURE 3.2.16 Areas affected by the 1988 fires in Yellowstone National Park

CASE STUDY

Fire and the Yellowstone National Park

Fire is an important factor in the maintenance of several ecosystem types. It releases the nutrients which have accumulated in the dead biomass, assists in the release and germination of dormant seeds, removes substances which may be toxic to some plants, eliminates parasites and fungi, and stimulates the vegetative reproduction of some woody and herbaceous species. Communities subject to fire often show a wider variety of species. Species that are adapted to frequent fires, by having a thickened bark, releasing seeds, or producing new growth are termed *pyrophytes*. Fires may be:

1 Ground fires which affect the subsurface organic/peat layer, damaging tree roots.
2 Surface fires affecting the surface leaf litter.
3 Dependent crown fires, where the tree canopy is ignited by surface fire.
4 Running crown fires, which are independent of the surface fire, as the heat from one tree ignites adjacent trees and may result in 'fire storm' conditions with temperatures up to 1000 degrees C.

The mountain or montane coniferous forests on the slopes of the coastal ranges and Rockies in the western US experience frequent fires either from natural sources such as lightning strikes, or as a result of human activities. Yellowstone National Park (YNP), the first national park in the US, was created in 1872, and covers an area of 8992 square

kilometres. Eighty per cent of the forest in the park consists of dense stands of tall lodgepole pine, with the remainder being composed of Englemann spruce and subalpine fir.

In 1972, the Wildland Fire Management Plan for Yellowstone National Park was introduced, as a result of which 1376 square kilometres were designated 'natural burn areas'. If a fire occurred in these areas, unless it was a risk to human life it would be allowed to burn out. By 1976, these areas had been extended to cover 6880 square kilometres (77 per cent of the park). Between 1972 and 1987, only 137 square kilometres had been burnt. In 1988, the months of June and July were very dry, and on the 15 July the 'natural burn' policy was suspended. The dry conditions continued through August, with the fires becoming increasingly frequent, and by September were in danger of becoming out of control. Over 9500 firefighters, 100 fire engines and 117 aircraft, at a total cost of $120 000 000, were brought in to fight the fires, and with the help of rainfall the fires were brought under control in late September. Fifty-eight per cent of the tree canopy had been burnt, with 10 000 acres so severely burnt that all the vegetation had been destroyed and the soil 'sterilized'.

STUDENT ACTIVITY 3.15
Assess the effectiveness of the 'natural burn' policy in Yellowstone National Park.

4
GLOBAL ECOSYSTEMS — GRASSLANDS, DESERTS, TUNDRA AND MARINE

Key Ideas

■ Temperate interior grasslands are associated with fertile chernozem or prairie soils, which have resulted in them being used for commercial agriculture.
■ Tropical savanna grasslands occur on less fertile ferruginous soils, and in areas with a more unreliable pattern of rainfall. In these areas land degradation may be a problem.
■ Pollution and over fishing are major threats to most marine ecosystems.

■ Marine areas vary considerably in their productivity with the highest occurring on coral reefs and nutrient rich upwelling zones associated with cold ocean currents.
■ Ecosystems in 'extreme' areas such as deserts and the tundra are fragile, and are being affected directly by developments including mining, and indirectly through atmospheric pollution.

Considerable controversy surrounds the origin of the major areas of both temperate and tropical grasslands. They may represent natural climax communities, or they may be the product of human activities, especially fire. Grasses are a major sub-type of herbaceous plants. They may be *annuals*, with a life cycle completed in one year, *biennials*, which begin their growth in one year and flower and produce seed in the following year, and *perennials*, which grow for several years. Grasses usually form an herb layer under trees, but in grasslands they are the dominants.

4.1 Tropical grassland ecosystems

The majority of tropical grasslands, occur in regions with a tropical savanna (tropical summer rain) type of climate. They are found between, approximately, 5° and 20° north and south of the Equator and are most extensive in Africa, stretching in a horseshoe shape from Senegal in the west, to Kenya in the east, and south into Botswana and Namibia.

In South America they are found in the Orinoco valley in Venezuela, where they are known as the *Llanos*, and over much of the Brazilian Plateau forming the *Campos*. In India they occur on the Deccan Plateau, and in Australia they are found in the north central parts of Queensland and the Northern Territory.

FIGURE 4.1.1 Tropical savanna climate

Tropical Savanna Climates			Jan	Feb	Mar	Apl	May	June	July	Aug	Sep	Oct	Nov	Dec	
Kayes	Latitude 14 N	Rainfall mm	–	–	–	–	15	99	211	211	142	48	8	5	Total 739 mm
	Altitude 61 m	Temp C	25	27	32	35	36	33	29	28	28	30	29	25	Range 11C
Daly															
Waters	Latitude 16 S	Rainfall mm	165	152	122	23	5	8	3	3	5	20	56	102	Total 664 mm
(Australia)	Altitude 210 m	Temp C	30	29	28	27	23	21	21	22	27	30	31	31	Range 10 C

Tropical Savanna Climate and Soils

The distinctive seasonal character of the climate of these areas results in soil water moving down through the soil profile in the summer wet season, but in the opposite direction during the winter dry season or in a dry summer. During the wet season, organic acids produced at the surface by the decomposition of plant and animal matter cause silica to move down through the soil profile. Iron and aluminium oxides (sesquioxides) may accumulate in the upper eluviated horizon, giving these *ferruginous* soils their characteristic red or yellow colour, or may together with clay, move into the illuviated B-horizon. In winter, during the dry season, capillarity may cause silica and iron to move up through the soil profile, to be deposited in one of the upper horizons (Figure 4.1.2). This concentration of iron or silica may lead to the formation of a narrow horizon, termed laterite (iron) or silcrete (silica), which if exposed at the surface hardens producing a duricrust.

Plants and animals of the Tropical Savanna

For many people their image of the savanna is one of continuous grasslands, with the occasional tree. Although that image is true for many areas, as with other biomes, there is, in reality, a very large range of habitats (Figure 4.1.3). At a sub-continental scale, as for example in West Africa, it is possible to identify a series of vegetation zones, related to total rainfall, and the length of the dry season (Figure 4.1.4). In the south, where the annual rainfall is over 900 mm, and the dry season is over 4 months, tropical rainforest is replaced by Guinea savanna. This consists of tropical deciduous seasonal forest, with mainly deciduous trees of between 6–15 m, which lose their leaves in the winter dry season, and tall grasses, in the case of elephant grass up to 5 m in height. Where the rainfall is between 600 and 900 mm, and the dry season is up to 7 months, the Guinea savanna is replaced by Sudan savanna. Here, the trees occur as individuals or small stands, together with grasses up to 1.5 m. Further inland to the north, conditions become more extreme, with the rainfall being reduced to between 250 and 600 mm, and the dry season extends for more than eight months. This is the *Sahel* savanna, where the vegetation consists of small thorny bushes together with several species of acacia tree forming thorn woodland, and grasses below one metre in height.

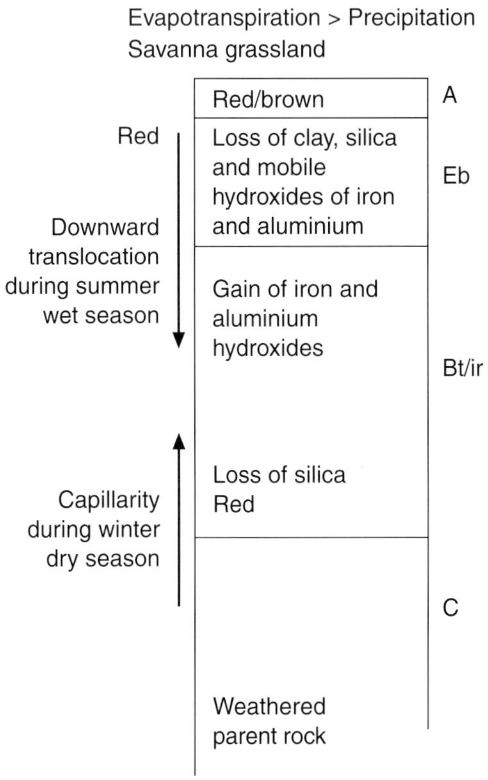

This variability is also seen in the net primary productivity (NPP). Although the average NPP is 900 g/sq.m/yr, values range from approximately 300 g/sq.m/yr in the dry Sahel savanna areas of the desert margins, to 1500 g/sq.m/yr in the tropical seasonal forest areas of the Guinea savanna.

As conditions become drier, the vegetation is increasingly **xerophytic**. In the seasonal forest, trees lose their leaves during the winter drought. In the more arid Sudan and Sahel zones, trees such as the baobab or 'bottle tree' occur, which are able to store water in their trunks. Succulents, euphorbias, which are similar to cacti, are also able to store moisture. Some trees have extensive shallow root systems to maximise the use of any rainfall, while others have deep tap roots, which are able to reach the water table. Many trees, and shrubs, reduce transpiration by having thorns instead of leaves.

At a local scale it is clear that the savanna is a complex mosaic of different habitats. Along the river channel a semi-evergreen gallery forest often develops, and on the steeper slopes are areas of savanna woodland. On the higher level plateau surfaces tussock grassland occurs, with savanna parkland (open savanna woodland and tall grasses) on the lower gentle slopes. The origin of these tropical grasslands is debatable. Some authorities maintain that they are the product of either natural or human fires. Many trees, including the baobab, are pyrophytic in that they have thick bark and other mechanisms to protect them against fire. Others maintain that they are the product of climatic change or soil factors.

A wide variety of animals, especially in Africa, exploit the wide range of habitats available in the savanna (Figure 4.1.3). The grasslands provide a variety of ecological niches. Elephants and giraffe are able to browse on the lower branches of trees and shrubs. The taller grasses are, initially, browsed by buffalo. The shorter grasses remaining are then grazed by wildebeest, followed by zebra, with gazelles cropping the short turf.

FIGURE 4.1.2 Ferruginous (savanna) soil

Evapotranspiration > Precipitation
Savanna grassland

	Red/brown	A
Red	Loss of clay, silica and mobile hydroxides of iron and aluminium	Eb
Downward translocation during summer wet season ↓	Gain of iron and aluminium hydroxides	Bt/ir
Capillarity during winter dry season ↑	Loss of silica Red	
		C
	Weathered parent rock	

FIGURE 4.1.3 Habitats and ecological niches in the savanna

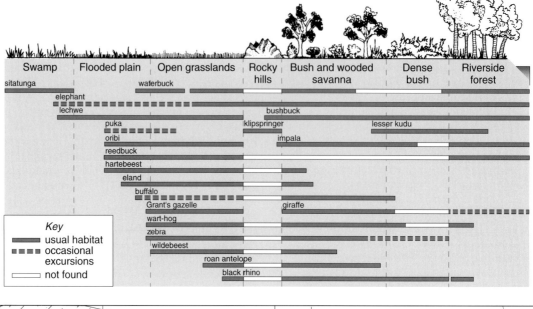

FIGURE 4.1.4 Vegetation zones of West Africa

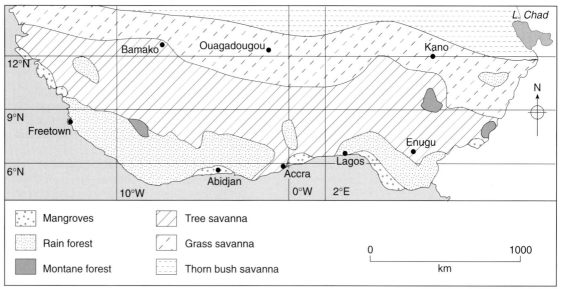

FIGURE 4.1.5 The height of savanna vegetation

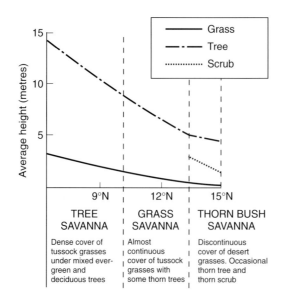

Wart hogs then root among the remaining grass. Grasslands near to rivers will also be grazed by hippopotamus. The large number of herbivores provide food for a range of predators, hunting alone, for example, leopard and cheetah, as a family as in the case of a pride of lions, as a pack (jackals and hyenas) or a flock (vultures). Insects are also numerous, especially locusts, grasshoppers, ants and termites. Termites are important decomposers (they are able to consume 30 kg of cellulose per hectare) and in some areas are so numerous (12 kg per hectare), that the presence of their hills leads to the formation of 'termite savanna'. In these areas there may be up to 600 termite hills per hectare.

STUDENT ACTIVITY 4.1

With reference to Figures 4.1.4, 4.1.5 and an atlas, analyse the pattern of vegetation in West Africa.

Explain how the seasonality of the tropical savanna climate affects its soils, plants and wildlife.

FIGURE 4.1.8

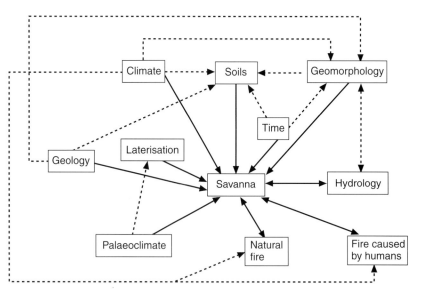

FIGURE 4.1.6 Factors affecting the formation of savanna grasslands

Teeming life of African savanna stuns biologists

A scientific meeting tomorrow will reveal something entirely unexpected: that the arid African savanna could be as rich and diverse a habitat as any rainforest or coral reef.

The Mkomazi game reserve in the Tanzanian uplands is home to 450 species of birds, 1000 species of plants and probably 90,000 kinds of insects and spiders. 'In a study from the Thailand rainforest in 1989 we get 123–256 individual insects per metre squared' said Dr George McGavin, an Oxford entomologist, 'but our work at Mkomazi is running at 660 individuals per metre squared'. 'It's the small creatures that make the ecology work. If you look after the insects everything else will look after itself'.

Guardian 25 May 1998

FIGURE 4.1.7 Savanna habitats

CASE STUDY

The National Parks of Southern Africa

Kenya, Tanzania, Zambia, Zimbabwe, Botswana, Namibia and South Africa all have extensive areas devoted to national parks or game reserves. The majority of these areas were created after World War II as concern grew over the decline in the numbers of key savanna species including the elephant, black rhinoceros, cheetah and leopard. The past 50 years have provided several examples of the difficulties involved in trying to manage wild game, and the interaction between them and local human populations.

Wild game such as zebra and wildebeest naturally migrate over large areas in search of water and grazing, usually following a seasonal cycle related to the location and date of the wet season. Many of the human populations, including the Masai, are pastoral nomads who also migrate with their cattle. The creation of national parks restricts the movements of people such as the Masai, limiting their grazing areas, often resulting in the overgrazing of the remaining grasslands, and causing them to be resentful of the protected animals in the parks.

The situation in the Kenyan National Park of Tsavo illustrates the need for the protection of endangered species. As a result of a combination of drought and poaching, between 1960 and 1989, when the trade in elephant and rhinoceros parts was made illegal by the Convention on International Trade in Endangered Species of Wild Fauna and Flora (CITES), the number of elephants decreased, from 40 000 to only 10 000. In other parks however the situation is very different. David Western, the Director of the Kenyan Wildlife Service was, in 1998, reported as saying that elephants are ecological vandals, capable of turning thick bush into desert faster than humans. He was referring to their impact on the Amboseli National Park in Kenya. Many animals in the park, protected from predation, and restricted in their migration, have rapidly multiplied to numbers which are so high that they are destroying their own habitats, and exceeding the carrying capacity of the ecosystem. The park has approximately 1000 elephants, and over the past 25 years much of its area has changed from wooded to grass savanna.

An adult elephant on average consumes 180 to 225 kg of plant material, and destroys or uproots an additional 270 kg per day. In the summer wet season they are able to browse on grass, but in the dry season they eat leaves, branches and bark, frequently ring barking trees causing them to die. One suggestion for the control of elephant numbers, if they cannot be moved to other parks or reserves, is 'crisis culling', followed by 'control culling'. This could be linked to the concept of the 'game crop', where carefully regulated sport or commercial hunting under licence would provide additional revenue for conservation. The decline of the woodland has caused other browsers, including rhinoceros and impala to decline, whereas grazers such as zebra, antelope and Cape buffalo have increased.

The decline of the woodland is also a consequence of the Masai not being permitted to graze their cattle in the park. Normally, elephants and other browsers would eat the bush, then the cattle would move in, keeping the grass short and allowing tree seedlings to grow. At any one time two-thirds of Kenya's large animals are outside the parks, and it is becoming clear that a policy of trying to contain them within fixed limits has produced unforeseen consequences. An alternative solution being tried in Kenya is to integrate the wildlife with the areas outside the parks. This involves the cooperation of local people, and legislation is proposed to integrate the Masai into conservation by:

- allowing them to cull troublesome animals as many elephants have lost their fear of people and invade farms for food, and since 1993 have killed 50 people,
- enable them to build high voltage fences around their fields and settlements,
- repair water holes damaged by animals,
- protect wooded areas,
- provide assistance for them to set up wildlife sanctuaries and provide tourist facilities (the first Masai tourist lodge was built, in 1996, at Ilngwesi), and
- carry out controlled grass burning at the start of the dry season.

In March 1998, the Kruger National Park, in the north east of South Africa, celebrated its centenary. The Park is approximately the size of Wales, and covers 2 m hectares. It has a wider range of habitats, and more species than any other park in Africa. The Park contains the 'magnificent seven' species i.e. buffalo (19 000), cheetah, elephant (8000), leopard, lion (2000), rhino (2200), and wild dog, together with over 600 bird species. As a consequence of its

FIGURE 4.1.9 Selected environmental features of the Kruger National Park

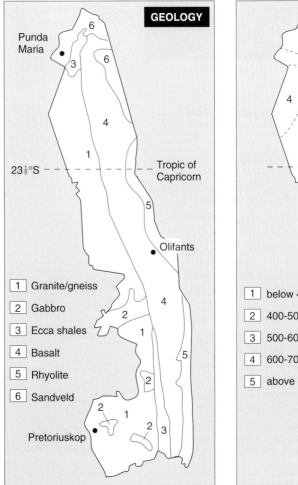

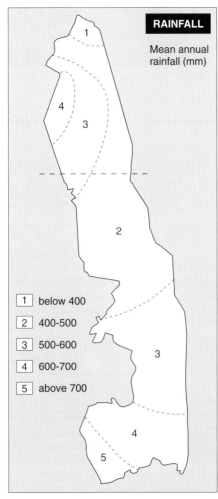

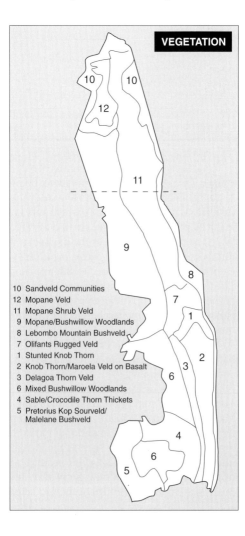

wildlife and landscape it is a popular tourist destination, with visitor numbers having increased from 30 000 in 1935 to 2.5 m in 1997. The winter dry season between April–September is the popular tourist season as the wildlife concentrate around the rivers and water holes.

The creation of the Park, and the consequent increase in both visitors and wildlife, has placed additional pressures on the Park's habitats. Overgrazing can lead to land degradation and the encroachment of bush onto the savanna grassland. Access roads and waterholes are being increasingly affected by the increasing use of 4×4 vehicles to transport visitors to the popular sites. The response of the Park authorities to these problems has included:

■ a controlled burning programme, on a 3–4 year cycle, to improve the carrying capacity of the grassland and to check bush encroachment,
■ the control of alien (exotic) species and plants considered as 'weeds', such as the cactus *Opuntia stricta*, which has invaded 16 000 hectares. Its seeds are spread in the faeces of elephants and baboons, after they have eaten the plant,
■ soil erosion has produced deep gullies or 'dongas', and these are being restored by the gully heads being covered by wood and brush, which allows sediment to accumulate and plants to grow.

■ erosion, around waterholes, is controlled by opening and closing them, as appropriate, in relation to the need of the animals and the amount of damage,
■ many of the fences surrounding the Park, for example the one separating it from the adjacent Sabi Sabi Reserve, are being removed to extend the wildlife migration routes,
■ regular game censuses are undertaken.

When the Park was created many local people lost access to traditional tribal lands they had used for game hunting, collecting timber for fuel and as a building material and water sources. Inevitably, this has led to resentment, and many tribes are seeking to have their lands reinstated. In 1998, the Makuleke community, near the Zimbabwean border, had 30 000 hectares reinstated, which will be jointly managed with the Park authorities as a tourism attraction with wilderness trails and tented camps.

STUDENT ACTIVITY 4.3

1 Refer to Figure 4.1.9 and describe the pattern of vegetation in the Kruger National Park.
2 To what extent does it appear to have been influenced by (i) geology and (ii) rainfall?
3 Outline some of the problems involved in managing a game reserve such as the Kruger.

CASE STUDY

Desertification

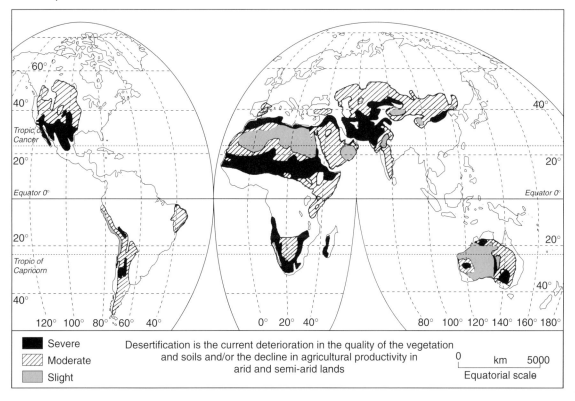

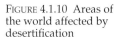

FIGURE 4.1.10 Areas of the world affected by desertification

■ Severe
▨ Moderate
▨ Slight

Desertification is the current deterioration in the quality of the vegetation and soils and/or the decline in agricultural productivity in arid and semi-arid lands

0   km   5000
Equatorial scale

FIGURE 4.1.11 Criteria for the identification of desertification

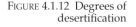

An increase in:	A decrease in:
Surface albedo	Key plant species
Soil compaction	Key animal species
Dust storms	Net primary productivity
Soil salinity	Biomass
Sand dune movement	Soil organic matter

Many savanna grassland areas are reportedly suffering from '*desertification*'. In 1991, desertification was described by the United Nations Environment Programme (UNEP) as 'land degradation in arid, semi-arid and dry subhumid areas, caused by adverse human impact'. In 1992, however, the United Nations Conference on Environment and Development (UNCED) defined it as 'land degradation in arid, semi-arid and dry subhumid areas, resulting from various factors including climatic variations and human activities'. The latter definition illustrates the key problem is desertification, a natural climatic process, the result of human activities, or a combination of the two?

Desertification may be indicated by several criteria (Figure 4.1.11), and is most likely to occur in semi-arid areas where precipitation is unreliable and between 250 and 400 mm per year. The severity of desertification varies, and Figure 4.1.12 indicates some of the effects of increasing levels of desertification on four variables.

The Sahel

The Sahel is the northern semi-arid zone of the savanna in Africa, to the south of the Sahara Desert. It has been extensively studied, and in 1975 H Lamprey suggested that the Sahara had extended south by 90 to 100 km between 1958 and 1975. Although recent satellite information has cast doubt on the 'rate' of desertification in the Sahel, significant areas of savanna have been lost. The reasons are complex (Figure 4.1.13), but include human factors such as overcultivation, overgrazing, salinisation resulting from excessive irrigation raising the water table, and deforestation to obtain

FIGURE 4.1.12 Degrees of desertification

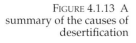

	Slight	Moderate	Severe	Very severe
Plant cover	Excellent to good	Fair range	Poor range	Surface almost denuded of vegetation
Erosion	None to slight	Moderate sheet erosion Shallow gullies	Severe sheet erosion Gullies common Occasional blow outs	Severely gullied Numerous blow outs
Salinisation	$<4 \times 10^3$ (mmhos)	4 to 8	8 to 15	Thick salt crust
Crop yields	Reduced by less than 10 per cent	Reduced by 10 to 50 per cent	Reduced by 50 to 90 per cent	Reduced by more than 90 per cent
World's sq. km drylands % area	24 520 000 52.1	13 770 000 29.3	8 700 000 18.5	73 000 0.1

FIGURE 4.1.13 A summary of the causes of desertification

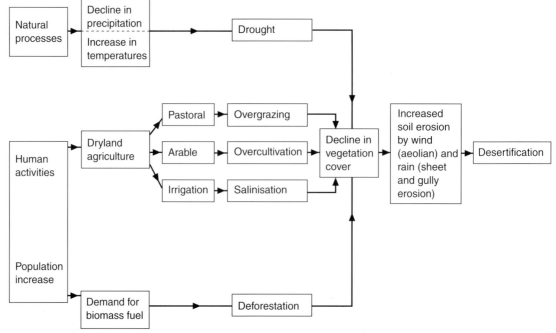

Reduce overcultivation	Reduce overgrazing	Reduce deforestation	Improve soil conditions	Alter social and economic conditions
■ Use fertilisers to increase yields ■ Use high yielding/drought resistant crop varieties ■ Use crop rotations ■ Use irrigation in the dry season	■ Improve grazing through controlled burning of grasslands ■ Introduce new breeds ■ Improve the medical care of the stock ■ Rotate grazing areas ■ Introduce game ranching	■ Use agroforestry (a combination of agriculture and forestry) ■ Tree planting schemes (Majjia Valley Project Niger) ■ Introduce alternative sources of fuels and building materials	■ Use natural mulches or plastic sheets to trap moisture ■ Build low stone or earth walls parallel to the contours to trap sediment and surface runoff (Burkino Faso) ■ Plant leguminous crops to add nitrogen ■ Reduce the effects of salinisation ■ Add fertilisers and organic material	■ Decrease the dependence on subsistence agriculture either by introducing commercial agriculture or developing craft and agricultural based industries ■ Extend tourism ■ Provide loans and grants

FIGURE 4.1.14 The management of desertification

timber for fuel and burning. The main natural factor is drought, although the term dessication is also used for long periods of drought. In the period 1960 to 1990, precipitation in the Sahel was between 20 and 40 per cent lower than that between 1931 and 1960. This could be due to climatic change involving the failure of the Inter Tropical Convergence Zone, a rain bearing low pressure cloud belt, to move as far north as 'normal', or a product of 'biogeophysical' feedback related to human induced land degradation.

STUDENT ACTIVITY 4.4

1 Refer to Figure 4.1.10 and describe the distribution of the areas affected by desertification.
2 Why is it difficult to identify areas affected by desertification?
3 To what extent is desertification a product of human activities?
4 Outline the main ways by which the problems associated with desertification may be managed.

4.2 Temperate grassland ecosystems

Climate and Soils of Temperate Grasslands

Temperate grasslands occur in two main types of location. In North America and Eurasia, the Prairies and the Steppes are in the centre of large continents where there is a temperate interior type of climate. The Pampas in Argentina, the Veldt in South Africa, and the Murray-Darling lowlands in Australia are on the eastern side of continents and have a climate transitional between temperature interior and temperate east coast (Figure 4.2.1).

The temperate interior climate of these areas produces a zonal soil called a chernozem or 'black earth'. The dominant grass vegetation of this ecosystem type decomposes to produce a neutral or slightly alkaline mull type of humus, which is quickly incorporated by earthworms and other soil fauna into the upper horizon, producing a deep humus rich A horizon. Humus levels may be as high as 10 per cent at the surface, decreasing to 2 per cent at the base of the A horizon. The A horizon has a strong crumb/granular structure, and is

			Jan	Feb	Mar	Apl	May	June	July	Aug	Sep	Oct	Nov	Dec	
Winnipeg	Latitude 49 N	Rainfall mm	23	23	31	36	58	79	79	64	58	38	28	23	Total 540 mm
	Altitude 240 m	Temp C	−19	−17	−9	3	11	17	19	17	12	5	−6	−14	Range 38 C
Bahia Blanca (Argentina)	Latitude 38 S	Rainfall mm	43	56	64	58	31	23	25	25	41	56	53	48	Total 523 mm
	Altitude 29 m	Temp C	24	22	20	16	12	9	9	10	12	15	19	22	Range 15 C

FIGURE 4.2.1 The climates of temperate grasslands

FIGURE 4.2.2 Temperate grassland soils – chernozems

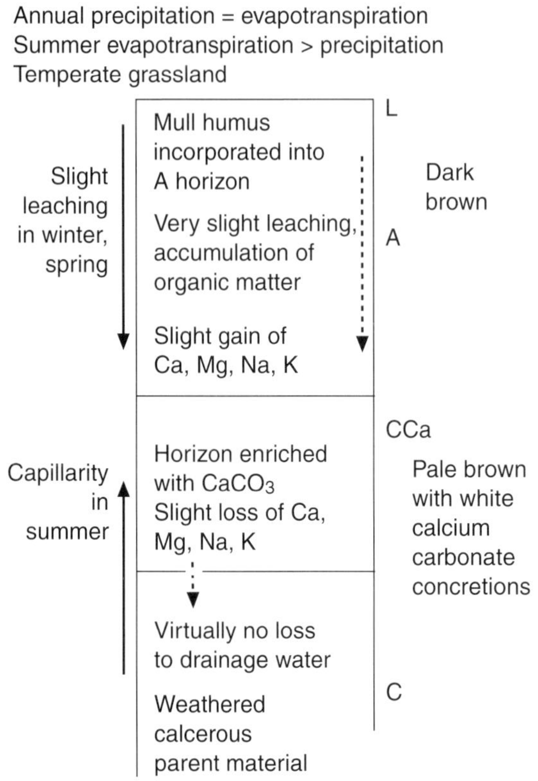

Annual precipitation = evapotranspiration
Summer evapotranspiration > precipitation
Temperate grassland

Slight leaching in winter, spring

Mull humus incorporated into A horizon

Very slight leaching, accumulation of organic matter

Slight gain of Ca, Mg, Na, K

L

Dark brown

A

Capillarity in summer

Horizon enriched with CaCO₃
Slight loss of Ca, Mg, Na, K

Virtually no loss to drainage water

Weathered calcerous parent material

CCa

Pale brown with white calcium carbonate concretions

C

extremely fertile. Mild leaching occurs in spring, following snow melt, but in summer, evaporation causes an upward movement of moisture, resulting in the precipitation of calcium carbonate in the C and B horizons (Cca/Bca). The depth of the B horizon is frequently limited, either by the nature of the parent rock, for example on calcium rich rocks such as limestone the chernozem may be a type of rendzina soil with no B horizon, or by the low levels of leaching. In the Northern Hemisphere, where the grassland/forest boundary occurs, due partly to the increase in precipitation, a leached chernozem or prairie soil occurs. This soil still has an organic rich humus A horizon, but also develops an illuvial brown coloured B horizon due to increased leaching. Where conditions become drier a chestnut soil develops, which has a similar structure to a chernozem but is shallower in depth.

CASE STUDY

The Prairies

FIGURE 4.2.3 Comparison of tropical and temperate grassland nutrient cycles

Ecosystem	Nutrient storage (kg/ha)			Annual nutrient transfer	
	Biomass	Litter	Soil	Soil to biomass	Biomass to litter
Tropical savanna grassland	978	300	502	319	312
Temperate grassland	540	370	5000	422	426

In the Great Plains of the USA it is possible to recognise three major grassland zones. In the west, where the annual precipitation is between 250 and 500 mm, and conditions are drier, short and bunch grass prairie occurs on a chestnut or chernozem soil. Grasses in this zone are between 0.15 and 0.45 metres in height and are mainly buffalo grass and blue grama grass. Further east, as the precipitation increases to between 500 and 1000 mm, mixed grasses, including little blue stem, needle grass and June grass reach heights of between 0.6 and 1.2 m. The tall grass prairie in the east has more than 1000 mm per year, and the big blue stem and switch grass reach heights of between 1.5 and 2.5 metres on a prairie soil. The average NPP of temperate grasslands is 600 g/sq.m/yr, and the average biomass 1600 g/sq.m/yr. Many of the grass species have very deep roots, up to 2 m, and consequently the majority of the biomass is underground.

Grasslands originally had very large numbers of a few species of large animals. On the Great Plains large herbivores, including bison and the pronghorn antelope, formed herds as protection from predators such as wolves and coyotes. Their numbers were however, greatly reduced in the nineteenth century as settlers moved further west.

STUDENT ACTIVITY 4.5

Refer to Figure 3.1.5, which shows Gersmehl's model of nutrient flow applied to the Equatorial rainforest.
1 Use the data in Figure 4.2.3 to draw similar graphs for both tropical savanna and temperate grasslands.
2 Analyse the differences in the nutrient cycles of the two ecosystems.

The small mammals of the grasslands include gophers, prairie dogs, and jack-rabbits, together with small birds such as meadowlarks and prairie chickens.

The generally fertile soils found beneath temperate grasslands have encouraged agriculture to be the dominant land use. On the Great Plains or Prairies of the US, extensive commercial grassland and arable farming systems are the two dominant types.

Extensive grassland farming or ranching occurs along the western margins, where drier conditions, with annual precipitation between 300 and 500 mm, restrict the growth of arable crops. Farms in these areas are large, normally with low fertiliser and energy inputs, and the major output being beef cattle. The grasslands tend to be of two types. Either, semi-natural 'unmanaged' grasslands consisting mainly of short grass species in the west, and mixed grass further east, or managed grasslands where rotational grazing, reseeding, controlled burning and fertiliser applications occur. Competition from other cattle producing areas, in Brazil and Argentina, has led to an intensification of the farming system. Normally, stocking rates are carefully controlled with reference to the age and type of the stock, and the annual grass yield (biomass). Usually, half the available forage land is ungrazed each year to allow regrowth. Stock is replenished by breeding, and a regulated number of cattle leave the system each year. The need to be profitable may result in overstocking, which in turn may lead to overgrazing. The consequent decrease in plant cover reduces the amount of organic material reincorporated into the soil and may result in soil erosion. The US Environmental Protection Agency (EPA), believe that livestock overgrazing is responsible for 28 per cent of the soil erosion in the western states. Overgrazing also allows other less desirable plant species, including the poisonous burroweed and woody species such as mesquite, sagebrush and juniper, to colonise the grasslands and form 'scrublands'. Much of the rangeland is owned by the federal government, and leased to the farmers. In 1993, the rate per head of cattle was increased in an attempt to reduce the stocking levels. In many areas, for example, Texas, irrigation is being used to allow the dry-lands to produce fodder crops, including alfalfa, for the cattle. The

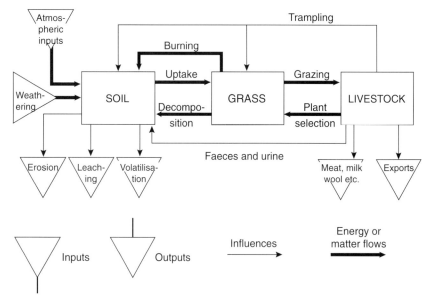

FIGURE 4.2.4 An extensive grassland farming system

circular irrigated areas produced by centre pivot systems are distinctive, and with other irrigation methods are causing local water tables to be significantly lowered. In the past, the Prairies were home to migrating herds of bison. In 1790, it was estimated that there were 30 m, a figure which declined to only 1000 in 1890. The present bison herd size is estimated at 250 000. Some conservationists maintain that commercial grazing should copy the grazing habits of the bison. Bison graze in large herds, for defence against predators such as wolves, and through their deposition of large quantities of dung and urine, fertilise the grazing zone. They also trample unpalatable species, and their large grazing range allows the grass to recover before the herd returns.

STUDENT ACTIVITY 4.6

Refer to Figure 4.2.4 and:
a) Describe and explain the following features of the system:
1 structure
2 inputs, and
3 outputs.
b) How does this ecosystem differ from a natural temperate grassland ecosystem?

FIGURE 4.2.5 Changes to temperate grasslands due to arable farming

Natural grasslands	Grasslands used for annual cereals
■ Mainly perennial grass species	■ Monoculture of annual cereals
■ Some annuals and bulb plants	■ Surface ploughed breaking up root mat
■ Soil surface composed of a dense root mat and present throughout the year	■ Reduction in soil moisture
■ Root mat retains moisture	■ Few roots to bind soil particles
■ Soil particles bound by roots	■ Increased loss of nutrients by leaching
■ Little loss of nutrients by leaching	■ Decrease in soil organic matter
■ Soil rich in organic matter	■ Increased wind erosion
■ Limited soil loss by wind erosion	■ Increased surface runoff and sheet erosion
■ Limited surface runoff and sheet erosion	■ Need for the application of inorganic fertilisers, herbicides, and pesticides

Extensive arable (crop) farming systems occur where precipitation is higher (over 500 mm). On the Prairies, wheat is the dominant crop, often grown as a monoculture. In Montana, and North and South Dakota it is spring wheat, with winter wheat in Kansas, Colorado and Oklahoma. Rotational cropping is becoming more frequent consisting of wheat, sorghum, and grass leys for sheep and cattle. Farms are large, highly mechanised, and use high yielding seed varieties together with high inputs of chemical fertiliser.

On the marginal western dry-lands, dry farming techniques are used to conserve soil moisture:

■ Weed growth is strictly controlled between harvesting and planting.

■ Upright wheat stubble is maintained through the winter to increase snow accumulation and reduce wind velocities.
■ A straw mulch is maintained until planting time, to decrease evaporation and surface runoff.
■ Plant residues are returned to the soil to maintain the nutrient cycle, and
■ Ploughing is kept to a minimum, with direct seed drilling.

STUDENT ACTIVITY 4.7

Describe and explain the effects that commercial (i) arable farming, and (ii) extensive ranching, have on the temperate grassland ecosystem.

Soil Erosion

Between 1933 and 1939, many parts of the Prairies suffered extreme soil erosion, resulting in the region being termed the 'Dust Bowl'. Dust storms called 'black blizzards' swept across the plains. They were the result of a combination of factors including a series of hot dry summers, long periods of strong winds, overgrazing, a rapid expansion of wheat farming, and the introduction of tractors. Soil erosion is a major world problem, with an annual total of 75 bn metric tonnes of soil being lost, and is a consequence of two main processes:

■ Wind (aeolian) erosion, and
■ Water (fluvial) erosion caused by splash erosion, sheet wash and rill (gully) erosion.

The rate of erosion depends upon a range of factors, including:

1 Rainfall – Intensity and duration.
2 Land use – Typical rates of erosion (in tonnes per hectare per year) in the Prairies are 0.2 from forested areas, 4 from grassy pastures, 54 from arable fields, and 450 from abandoned farmland affected by gully erosion.
3 Slope angle – As the angle increases, mass movement processes become more important,
4 Soil texture – Sandy and peaty soils have higher rates than clay soils,
5 Farming practices – The increasing use of chemical (inorganic) fertilisers, and the decrease in crop rotations, may result in a decrease in the organic content of soils and their ability to retain moisture. Other agricultural factors include the method and season of ploughing, the time of planting, the nature of the crop, field size, the use of heavy machinery, and stubble burning.

FIGURE 4.2.6 The effects of soil erosion

FIGURE 4.2.7 Wind erosion in Colorado (hectares)

Year	Cropland damage	Crops destroyed	Average farm size
1969	10988	56356	335
1972	29525	20011	
1975	261737	388189	428
1978	168083	76184	
1981	925830	19213	
1983	147187	31003	520

The primary effect of soil erosion is a loss of part of the upper soil horizon which normally contains large amounts of organic and nutrient rich material. Apart from affecting the soil itself, soil erosion also produces several secondary or off-site effects. These include the silting of reservoirs, increased flooding due to increased surface runoff and an increased sediment load in the river, and **eutrophication** due to the high nitrate levels in the runoff. A variety of soil conservation techniques are used to combat soil erosion:

> ### STUDENT ACTIVITY 4.8
> Prepare a short information pamphlet for farmers, which illustrates the causes and possible management of soil erosion.

FIGURE 4.2.8 Soil conservation techniques

Improve organic content	Improve moisture content	Reduce surface runoff	Reduce surface wind velocities	Reduce compaction
■ Use organic (farmyard manure) fertiliser ■ Reduce use of chemical (inorganic) fertilisers ■ Shallow plough or plough in crop stubble ■ Use crop rotations	■ Improve organic content ■ Use irrigation	■ Contour plough ■ Build drainage ditches at right angles to the slope ■ Terracing ■ Maintain crop or stubble cover ■ Maintain vegetation corridors along field boundaries or crop strips	■ Plant wind breaks ■ Limit field size	■ Reduce stock levels ■ Use wider tyres or double tyres on machinery

4.3 Desert (arid) ecosystems

Tropical desert climate and soils

FIGURE 4.3.1 Tropical desert climates

Tropical Desert Climate			Jan	Feb	Mar	Apl	May	June	July	Aug	Sep	Oct	Nov	Dec	
Khartoum	Latitude 15 N	Rainfall mm	–	–	–	–	3	8	53	71	18	5	–	–	Total 148 mm
	Altitude 390 m	Temp C	23	25	28	31	33	33	32	31	32	32	28	22	Range 11 C
Walvis Bay (Namibia)	Latitude 23 S	Rainfall mm	–	5	8	3	3	–	–	3	–	–	–	–	Total 22 mm
	Altitude 7 m	Temp C	19	19	19	18	17	16	14	14	14	18	17	18	Range 5 C

The lack of organic material in these areas is one of the factors which limits the development of 'true' soils. Many desert 'soils' are in fact raw mineral soils, composed mainly of inorganic materials particularly sands. They are azonal soils with a very limited development of soil horizons. Many of them show evidence of the upward movement (capillarity) of minerals, for example, calcium carbonate and silica, which often produce a surface deposit or 'duricrust'.

Sierozems are the main type of true desert soil, and may be either red or grey. They are shallow in depth, with a low organic content, and a high percentage of free calcium.

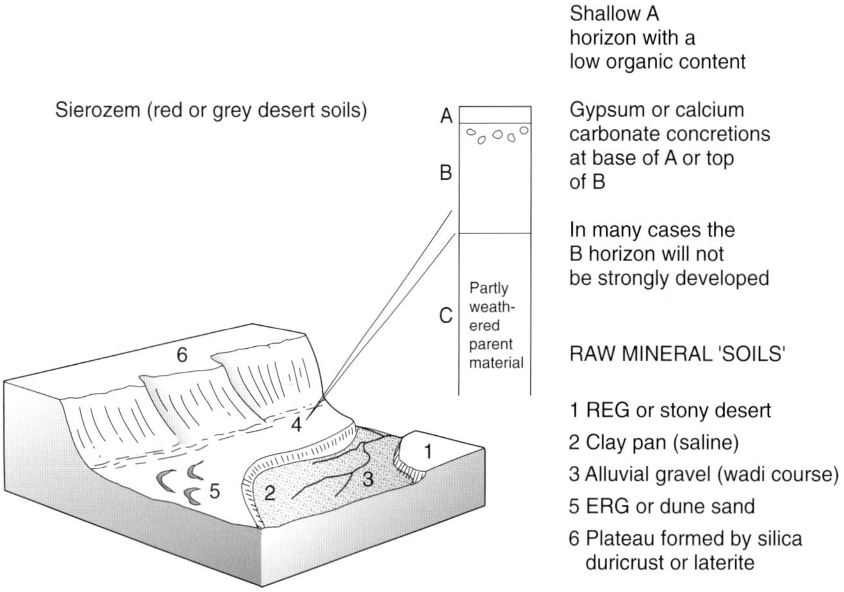

Sierozem (red or grey desert soils)

Shallow A horizon with a low organic content

Gypsum or calcium carbonate concretions at base of A or top of B

In many cases the B horizon will not be strongly developed

RAW MINERAL 'SOILS'

1 REG or stony desert
2 Clay pan (saline)
3 Alluvial gravel (wadi course)
5 ERG or dune sand
6 Plateau formed by silica duricrust or laterite

Partly weathered parent material

FIGURE 4.3.2 Desert soils – sierozems

The plants and animals of tropical deserts

FIGURE 4.3.3 Plant
adaptations to high
temperatures and
drought

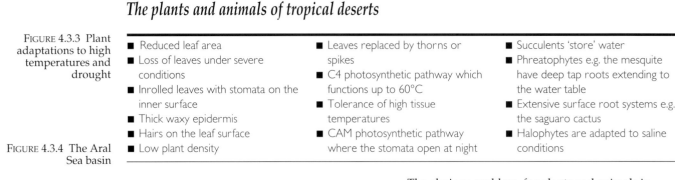

- Reduced leaf area
- Loss of leaves under severe conditions
- Inrolled leaves with stomata on the inner surface
- Thick waxy epidermis
- Hairs on the leaf surface
- Low plant density

- Leaves replaced by thorns or spikes
- C4 photosynthetic pathway which functions up to 60°C
- Tolerance of high tissue temperatures
- CAM photosynthetic pathway where the stomata open at night

- Succulents 'store' water
- Phreatophytes e.g. the mesquite have deep tap roots extending to the water table
- Extensive surface root systems e.g. the saguaro cactus
- Halophytes are adapted to saline conditions

FIGURE 4.3.4 The Aral
Sea basin

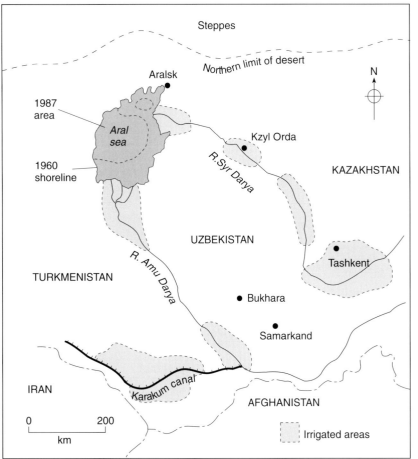

The obvious problem, for plants and animals in tropical deserts, is the lack of available water. Water is essential to circulate nutrients in the plant, to allow photosynthesis to take place, and to regulate plant temperature through transpiration. As water is limited in this type of environment, the majority of plants are **xerophytes**, which have various mechanisms to optimise water use (Figure 4.3.3).

At 90 g/sq.m./yr, the NPP of tropical deserts is the lowest of all the major land biomes. Up to 80 per cent of the NPP may be underground with green plant material only being 1 per cent of total NPP. Perennial plants in desert ecosystems are often succulents, for example, euphorbias in Africa and cacti in North America, and may be dwarfed and woody. The annuals or *ephemerals*, have a short life cycle, commencing after rain, during which they flower and produce seeds which then lie dormant until the next rainstorm.

Desert animals have also developed a variety of mechanisms to allow them to exist in such a harsh environment. Many of the birds migrate during the hot summer. A large number of animals, especially those with moist or porous skins, are nocturnal. The kangaroo rat spends the day in its burrow in the ground, emerging at night to feed. Specific adaptations include the large ears of the Jack Rabbit, which help to remove excess heat, and *'aestivation'*, a form of hibernation. For example, the spadefoot toad, which during the summer burrows into the sand, and lowers its body temperature and metabolic rate.

CASE STUDY

The Aral Sea – The Impact of Irrigation in an Arid Environment

The Aral Sea is an inland saline sea, located in an arid area, at approximately 45° north, in the western part of the Republic of Kazakhstan, and the northern part of Uzbekistan.
Data collected over the past 40 years has clearly shown that the level of the Aral Sea is falling. In 1960 it was 53.75 m, but by 1987 it had fallen to 40.50 m. Over the same time period, its area had decreased from 58 000 sq. km to 41 000 sq. km, and its volume from 1090 cu km to 374 cu km. The debate is whether, or not, this is a natural trend, due

to climatic change, or whether it is due to human (anthropogenic) activities, or both. The Aral Sea needs 42 to 44 cu km of water annually, to maintain its level. Of this, approximately 15 cu km comes from rainfall. In the past, about 70 cu km was provided by two large rivers, the Amu Darya and Syr Darya, draining from the Pamir Mountains to the south. From 1918, as part of the former Soviet Union's desire to develop agriculture, large areas of the two republics were irrigated, using water from the two rivers. In 1950, 2 m hectares were irrigated,

Year	Level (metres)	Area 000 sq.km	Volume cu.km	Salinity g/l	Inflow Amu Darya cu.km	Inflow Syr Darya cu.km	Total Inflow cu.km	Evapora-tion loss cu.km	Net change cu.km
1960	53.75	58.0	1090	10	37.8	21.0	58.8	64.1	−5.3
1971	51.05	60.2	925	12	15.3	8.1	23.4		
1976	48.28	55.7	763	14	10.3	0.5	10.8		
1987	40.50	41.0	374	27			2.0	56.2	−54.2
2000	33.00	23.4	162	35					

FIGURE 4.3.5 Changes in the hydrology of the Aral Sea

and by 1988 it had reached 7.2 m hectares. These irrigated areas were used to provide the former Soviet Union with 95 per cent of its cotton, 40 per cent of its rice, and 35 per cent of its fruit. In the Aral Sea basin, 90 per cent of all agricultural produce comes from irrigated land.

The data on the discharge (inflow) from the two rivers (Figure 4.3.5) indicates the size of the reduction in flow. In the case of the Amu Darya, one of the major causes of the decrease in discharge has been the Karakum Canal, at 1300 kms it is the longest and largest in the former USSR. At one time 14 sq km of water per year was been withdrawn from the Amu Darya, through the Karakum Canal, to irrigate the Kakakum Desert. Between 1956 and 1986, a total of 225 sq km of water was diverted from the Amu Darya. In addition, from 1945, large quantities of pesticides, herbicides, and fertilisers were used to maximise the production of the agricultural crops. These have added to the deterioration of the quality of the water, as they are becoming more highly concentrated, as a consequence of the decreased discharge of the two rivers.

The impact of the decrease in size of the Aral Sea, and of the discharge from the two rivers has resulted in significant changes to the environment:

1   Between 1957 and 1980, the number of fish species in the Aral Sea has declined from 24 to 4. In the same time period, the total fish catch has fallen from 48 000 metric tonnes per year to virtually zero. Originally, Muinak was a fishing port on the coast of the sea, now it is 48 km inland, and the fishing industry has declined.
2   The deltas of the Amu and Syr Darya rivers have been particularly affected by the decrease in the level of the Aral Sea, and by the related fall of between 3 and 8 m in the water table. These sensitive wetland habitats have seen major changes in their plant communities as salinity levels increase. The Tugay forests, once covered 260 000 hectares of the Amu Darya delta. They have now been reduced to 50 000 hectares. The 300 000 hectares of lakes and bogs of the Amu delta have nearly all dried up, and reeds which initially covered 700 000 hectares have almost disappeared. Local animal species have also been affected. Originally, there were 173 animal species, including wild boar, jackal, deer, and muskrat in the deltas, now the figure is 38.

FIGURE 4.3.6 The Aral Sea

3   Water loss from unlined irrigation channels and the uncontrolled use of irrigation water has in some areas caused the water table to rise. This has led to waterlogging of the soil, and as temperatures are very high during the summer, salts have been drawn to the soil surface and deposited as the water is evaporated, leading to the salinisation of the soil. It has been estimated that 5 m hectares has become saline.
4   Between 1960 and 1990, 27 000 sq km of the sea bed has been exposed, most of which was covered by various salts including calcium sulphate, sodium chloride, sodium sulphate and magnesium chloride. Since 1975, large quantities of this salt have been blown by the wind, forming salt storms, sometimes 40 km wide and 320 km long, which have been recorded up to 1000 km away in the Fergama Valley in Georgia. Mixed in with the salts are pesticide, herbicide and fertiliser residues, which are believed to be responsible for the increase in the cases of cancer, respiratory and eye problems, and deformed babies among the local people.
5   The Aral Sea affects the local climate up to a distance of 300 km. Its shrinkage have been associated with increasing 'desertification' in the area. Precipitation has decreased, summer temperatures have increased, and winter temperatures have decreased.

A variety of solutions, have been proposed to reverse the fall in the level of the Aral Sea:

1 Inter-basin water transfer – This was perhaps the most ambitious scheme. The aim of the scheme was to divert water from the rivers Ob and Irtysh in Siberia into the Aral Sea. It was suspended by President Gorbachev in 1985, who felt it was not cost effective.
2 Improvements in irrigation efficiency – The ratio of irrigation water used productively on the land, to the amount of water withdrawn from water sources, gives the level of irrigation efficiency. In the 1980s it was approximately 60 per cent, and the aim is to increase that figure to 75 per cent.
3 Recycle water from the irrigation systems back to the Aral Sea – In the 1980s, approximately 34 cu km of water was abstracted annually from the rivers Amu and Syr Darya. Twenty-one cu km was returned to the rivers, with the remaining 13 cu km being lost through evaporation or into groundwater. The drainage water is saline (3g/l), and contaminated by pesticides, herbicides,

phosphates, and nitrates. Consequently, it needs to be purified before re-use.
4 Improve the Aral Sea deltas – One idea to improve these regions is to build embankments in the Aral Sea, creating polders, where the water level would be maintained 8 m above the present water level.
5 Plant exposed areas of the sea bed with salt tolerant (halophytic) species to reduce wind erosion.
6 Improve the use of existing irrigated areas through technology, crop rotation, and the use of high yielding crop varieties.

STUDENT ACTIVITY 4.9

1 Use the Aral Sea case study to outline the problems involved in introducing commercial agriculture into an arid area.
2 Suggest how these problems may be overcome.

4.4 Tundra ecosystems

The climate and soils of tundra ecosystems

In many parts of the tundra there are few true zonal soils, instead the conditions of extreme frost or waterlogging produce azonal soils as on screes, or intrazonal soils, for example in waterlogged valley bottoms. In these periglacial areas, the very low winter temperatures produce a zone of permanently frozen ground, or permafrost. In summer, the upper part or active zone of permafrost does thaw, and the high water content means that even on gentle slopes, this zone may move down slope – a process called solifluction. The effect of frost also produces frost heave, causing the ground to be deformed, ice wedges and patterned ground to be formed, and stones to move upwards towards the surface, often producing stone circles or stripes. In depressions, and along river flood plains, water will accumulate above the impermeable permafrost producing waterlogged or gley conditions. The low oxygen or anaerobic conditions prevent the rapid decomposition of organic material, which accumulates forming peat. On the better drained slopes. a shallow *arctic brown earth* may form.

Plants and animals of tundra ecosystems

Although conditions are extreme in tundra ecosystems, the average NPP of 140 g/sq.m./yr is still higher than that in desert ecosystems. Tundra areas usually occur where the growing season is less than 3 months, and the mean daily temperature, in the warmest month, is below 10°C. The most favourable conditions are found at the forest-tundra boundary, where 'tree-tundra' consisting of isolated stands of birches, willows and alder occur. Conditions throughout much of the tundra, however, require that plants are adapted to strong winds, low summer temperatures, and a moisture deficit due to frozen ground. Specific habitats are strongly related to variations in relief (Figure 4.4.2).

Conditions in the Antarctic tundra are even more severe, and plant communities are dominated by lichens (400 species), mosses (75), and liverworts (20).

Plant life in tundra regions is limited by the low availability of nutrients. Consequently, nutrients are very quickly recycled. It has been estimated that

FIGURE 4.4.1 The tundra climate

Tundra climate			Jan	Feb	Mar	Apl	May	June	July	Aug	Sep	Oct	Nov	Dec	
Point Barrow (Alaska)	Latitude 71 N Altitude 8 m	Rainfall mm	5	5	3	3	3	8	22	17	12	15	8	8	Total 109 mm
		Temp C	−27	−27	−26	−18	−7	−1	2	4	4	0	−8	−24	Ranges 31 C
Churchill (Canada)	Latitude 59 N Altitude 13 m	Rainfall mm	13	15	23	23	23	48	56	69	58	36	25	18	Total 407 mm
		Temp C	−28	−27	−21	−10	−1	6	12	11	5	−3	−14	−24	Range 40 C

nitrogen is recycled eleven times a season, and phosphorus 200 times, that is, 3 times a day!

Figure 4.4.4 illustrates some of the ways in which plants and animals adapt to the conditions. Animal populations in the tundra are very cyclical. The population of snow-shoe hares reaches a peak after approximately 9 to 10 years. The population then 'crashes'. This growth cycle is paralleled by the hare's chief predator, the lynx, but with one year's time lag. Animals in the marine food chain, seals, walrus, skuas, gulls and polar bears, are normally more constant.

STUDENT ACTIVITY 4.10

With reference to Figure 4.4.2, to what extent is the vegetation of the tundra related to variations in relief and soil type?

FIGURE 4.4.3 The tundra environment

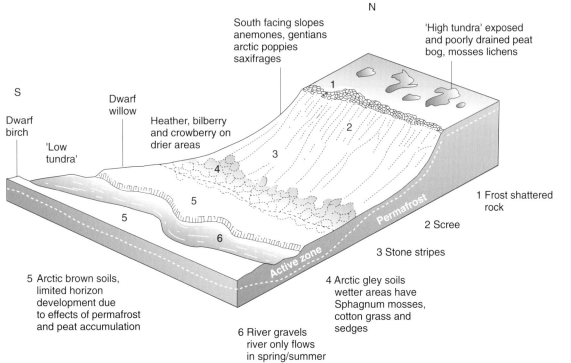

FIGURE 4.4.2 The environmental relationships between tundra vegetation and soils

N

South facing slopes anemones, gentians arctic poppies saxifrages

'High tundra' exposed and poorly drained peat bog, mosses lichens

S

Dwarf birch

'Low tundra'

Dwarf willow

Heather, bilberry and crowberry on drier areas

Permafrost

Active zone

1 Frost shattered rock

2 Scree

3 Stone stripes

4 Arctic gley soils wetter areas have Sphagnum mosses, cotton grass and sedges

5 Arctic brown soils, limited horizon development due to effects of permafrost and peat accumulation

6 River gravels river only flows in spring/summer

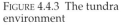

FIGURE 4.4.4 Plant and animal adaptations to tundra conditions

PLANTS		ANIMALS
■ Dwarfed forms (nanism)	■ Dormant seeds	■ Seasonal migration (caribou)
■ Prostrate habit	■ Carbohydrate storage organs (often underground) enable the plant to grow quickly in Spring	■ Hibernation (arctic ground squirrel)
■ Hemispherical cushion shape		■ Increased fur cover (musk-ox, arctic hare)
■ Tissues can tolerate intercellular ice	■ Flower buds formed one or more years before flowering	■ Enlarged foot pads (snow-shoe hare)
■ Some species can tolerate temperatures down to −80 °C	■ Photosynthesis can occur at very low temperatures	■ Fur colour change between summer and winter (arctic fox)
■ Small, dark coloured and long lived leaves	■ Quick turnover of mineral nutrients	■ Blubber layer (penguins, seals)

FIGURE 4.4.5 The tundra food web

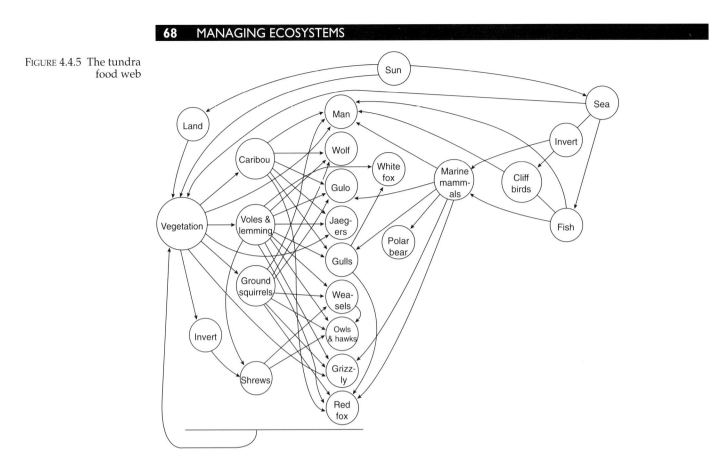

FIGURE 4.4.6 The location of the Arctic National Wildlife Refuge and National Petroleum Reserve, Alaska

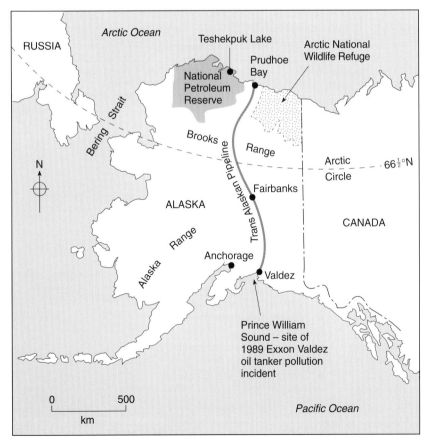

CASE STUDY

The Alaskan Tundra

Tundra ecosystems are sensitive to change, having low levels of resistance and resilience to disturbance. In Alaska they cover approximately half of the state, with lowland tundra north of the Yukon River, and mountain tundra along the Alaskan Range, including Mount McKinley, which at 6194 m is North America's highest mountain.

Like many other tundra areas, those in Alaska have been affected by a variety of human activities:

1 Military activities associated with the building of the Distant Early Warning (DEW) system.
2 Pollution – Increasing aerosol (particulate) pollution from other parts of North America and Europe frequently produce a pollution haze. There has also been an 8 per cent decline in the ozone layer over the Arctic. Research in 1998 indicated that the effect of the increase in greenhouse gas emissions has caused Alaska to warm by 1°C per decade over the past three decades, a figure, which is three times the Arctic average. The soil temperature, to a depth of one metre, has shown a similar rise. PCBs, DDT and other pesticide residues have in increasing quantities been found in animals such as polar bears at the top of the food chain (Figure 4.4.7).
3 Mineral and energy resources – Parts of the Alaskan tundra have been mined for gold and copper, but it is the expansion of oil and gas exploration which appears to be the larger threat to its ecosystems. In 1968, oil was discovered at Prudhoe Bay, on the North Slope.

The field is the largest in North America with seven production zones, and estimated reserves of 9 bn barrels. In 1969, with all the potential sea routes ice bound in winter, it was decided to export the oil by building the 1300 kilometre long Trans Alaska Pipeline System (TAPS) across Alaska, linking Prudhoe Bay with the ice free port of Valdez on the south coast. The first oil moved along the pipeline in 1977.

4 Transport developments – In 1974, the 666 km long Dalton Highway was built to support the construction of the pipeline. It links Livengood (near Fairbanks), with Deadhorse near Prudhoe Bay, to allow, approximately, 15 000 trucks per year, access to the oil fields. Both the pipeline and the Dalton Highway pass through the Gates of the Arctic National Park, and initially public access was restricted to its southern section. In 1994, the Alaska Supreme Court permitted the total length of the highway to be open to the public, increasing the threat from recreational activities along the North Slope.

The importance of the landscape and wildlife of Alaska has been recognised by the fact that 45 per cent of its area is protected as National Interest Lands (NIL). Created by the 1980 Alaska National Interest Lands Conservation Act (ANILCA), which amended the 1964 Wilderness Act, NIL areas consist of four types, National Parks, Preserves and Monuments, National Wildlife Refuges, National Forests and Bureau of Land Management areas.

The Arctic National Wildlife Refuge (ANWR) is one of 16 NWRs, and was, initially, designated in 1960 as the Arctic National Wildlife Range covering 3.56 m hectares. In 1980 it became the ANWR and extended to 7.6 m hectares. It includes three main types of ecosystem. Coniferous or taiga forest covers the South Slope of the Brooks Range with an arctic-alpine environment on the summits, and tundra on the North Slope. The ANWR is located to the east of the present oil fields, but in 1986 oil was discovered within the ANWR on section 1002 of the North Slope. The field is large, with an average estimate of 9.2 bn barrels, and if developed would be linked by a new pipeline to TAPS. Unfortunately, oil production, in the Prudhoe Bay area, will be halved by 2000, and by 2015 the oil field will no longer be viable. In 1992, the oil industry supported 86 per cent of the State of Alaska's $3 bn budget, and the extraction of oil from the ANWR would compensate for the decline of the Prudhoe Bay oil field. The proposal has not surprisingly caused a conflict of views between conservationists and those in favour of the development. The extraction of oil

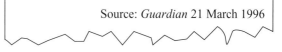
FIGURE 4.4.7

Toxic shocker

Last July, Canadian biologist David Schindler, from the University of Alberta, reported that turbot and trout in remote lakes in the Yukon contained levels of the pesticide toxaphene that were 10 times higher than Canadian food safety health limits. He also found high levels of DDT, a crop pesticide, PCBs (polychlorinated biphenyls, man-made chemicals once widely used in the electronics industry) and mercury in the fish.

Toxaphene has been banned in Canada for over a decade. The likely source is the soil of tropical Asia and Latin America, where toxaphene is a widely used pesticide. How did it get so far north?

Last September, Ronald Hites from the University of Indiana published a study of pesticides in tree bark at 90 sites worldwide. The pesticides most easily evaporating from soils turned up in the highest concentrations on the edges of the Arctic, thousands of kilometres from their source. The cold air of the Arctic acts as a cleansing system for the rest of the earth causing the pollutants to condense out of the atmosphere. Once the poisons reach Arctic waters, they concentrate further as biological processes take over. They reach their highest concentrations in animals at the top of the food chain, like birds, polar bears and humans. Many of the chemicals, including toxaphene, are compounds known as organochlorines, which accumulate in body fat. Scientists blame these for causing deaths among marine mammals, such as whales and seals, and for making some male mammals infertile.

Source: *Guardian* 21 March 1996

from the ANWR is supported by the Governor of Alaska and a lobby group known as Arctic Power. The Alaska Wilderness League, however, oppose any developments in the ANWR, or other NWRs. They are concerned that the ANWR will suffer similar environmental damage to that which has been reported from the Prudhoe Bay area.

In November 1992, Bill Clinton was elected the US President. Both he and his Vice-President Al Gore campaigned for stronger environmental controls, and legislation was passed providing short term protection for the ANWR. In August 1998, however, the US government announced that it was opening up 2 m ha of the north east quadrant of the National Petroleum Reserve, Alaska (located to the west of St. Prudhoe Bay) for oil production (Figure 4.4.6). Any developments in the Reserve would affect the coastal Teshekpuk Lake, and the Colville River delta wetland habitats.

STUDENT ACTIVITY 4.11

1 To what extent do you think that economic development should be allowed in tundra areas?
2 Why is the tundra such a fragile ecosystem?

4.5 Wetlands

Wetlands may be described as ecosystems whose formation, life processes and characteristics are dominated by water. They cover approximately 6 per cent of the Earth's surface, and include a variety of different habitats including swamps, marshes, mires, fens, peatlands, rivers, and lakes. These are all transitional habitats where land and water meet, and as such are examples of **ecotones**. Wetlands are important for:

1 Sedimentation: especially on deltas and flood plains, wetlands trap water, allowing the deposition of nutrient rich sediment, which often forms the basis for agriculture such as rice farming.

2 Pollution control: wetland plants and the associated bacteria are able to trap, and break down organic pollution, such as domestic sewage (Figure 4.5.1).

3 Flood protection: wetlands such as peatlands are capable of quickly storing water, but release it slowly, while as their height increases, salt marshes may protect coastlines.

4 Wildlife: many birds breed on, or during migration, use wetlands as sources of food.

5 Fuel and building materials: peat provides a source of fuel, and reeds and mangroves are used as building materials.

Wetlands are facing a variety of threats including:

■ destruction of habitats and their related plant and animal species, especially from urban and agricultural development,
■ drainage,
■ increased water abstraction from ground and surface waters,
■ pollution, nutrient enrichment and siltation,
■ modification or loss of physical features, for example from river channelisation,
■ introduction of non-native species,
■ intensive fisheries management,
■ inappropriate development of recreation and navigation.

In 1971, increasing concern over the rate of loss of wetlands, and the implications for a large number of species, especially of birds, which feed on them, resulted in 92 countries signing the Ramsar Convention. This obliges the countries to designate and protect wetlands of international importance. Seven hundred and seventy six wetland sites have so far been placed on the Ramsar list.

FIGURE 4.5.1 'The Kidneys of the Black Sea' – the Danube delta

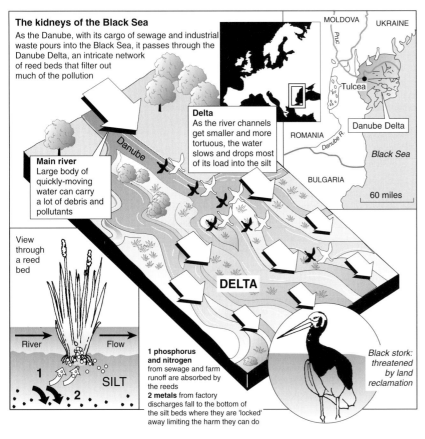

The kidneys of the Black Sea
As the Danube, with its cargo of sewage and industrial waste pours into the Black Sea, it passes through the Danube Delta, an intricate network of reed beds that filter out much of the pollution

Delta
As the river channels get smaller and more tortuous, the water slows and drops most of its load into the silt

Main river
Large body of quickly-moving water can carry a lot of debris and pollutants

View through a reed bed

River Flow

SILT

1 phosphorus and nitrogen from sewage and farm runoff are absorbed by the reeds
2 metals from factory discharges fall to the bottom of the silt beds where they are 'locked' away limiting the harm they can do

DELTA

Black stork: threatened by land reclamation

MOLDOVA UKRAINE

Prut

Tulcea

ROMANIA

Danube R.

Danube Delta

Black Sea

BULGARIA

60 miles

CASE STUDY

Louisiana Wetlands

The main areas of wetlands in Louisiana are along the flood plain and delta of the River Mississippi and the Louisiana coastal plain. The wetlands are important as they provide 30 per cent of the national fish harvest (menhaden, shrimps, blue crabs, oysters and crawfish), 30 per cent of the fur harvest (including muskrat and coypu), oil and gas, and are home to 66 per cent of the overwintering Mississippi Flyway bird population. They represent 40 per cent of the total area of coastal wetlands in the USA, and consist of a complex system of interrelated habitats (Figure 4.5.2):

■ Saline marsh consisting of halophytes such as *Spartina alterniflora*.
■ Brackish marshes, where the water is less saline, and the shorter and denser *Spartina patens* is able to grow.
■ Fresh water marshes with a wide variety of rushes, sedges and bog species.
■ Swamp forest consisting of bald cypresses, tupelo, water oak and water hickory.

The wetlands of Louisiana used to cover an area of approximately 6 m hectares. In recent decades the

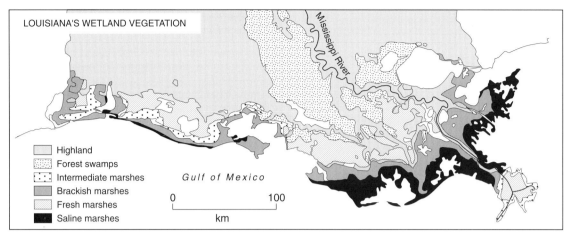

LOUISIANA'S WETLAND VEGETATION

Mississippi River

Gulf of Mexico

Highland
Forest swamps
Intermediate marshes
Brackish marshes
Fresh marshes
Saline marshes

0   100
km

FIGURE 4.5.2 The habitats of the Louisiana wetlands

area has been decreasing at an ever increasing rate. In the 1900s the decline was 0.25 per cent per year, a figure which had increased in the 1980s to 2 per cent or 100 sq km per year. The reasons for the decline are complex, but include:

1 A reduction in the amount of sediment deposited in the Mississippi delta – Since 1900 the size of the delta has been decreasing. It is believed that this decrease in the amount of sediment deposited, and the consequent reduction in the accumulation of organic material is a consequence of a variety of human activities which have taken place in the Mississippi's catchment area. Structures such as dams prevent the river from flooding but trap sediment in the reservoirs. Measures to reduce soil erosion, afforestation and the expansion of urban areas have all reduced the amount of sediment reaching the river. In 1963, the sediment load of the river at the delta was 434 000 000 tonnes per year. The figure has now decreased to only 255 000 000 tonnes, representing a 41 per cent reduction. There has also been a decrease in the size of sediment reaching the delta, as the coarser material is deposited in the reservoirs. As a result of channelisation, the increased velocity of the river carries the finer clays and silts further out to sea.
2 Increased subsidence – As the sediments accumulate, they are compacted causing the delta to subside by an average annual rate of 1.49 cm. This figure has been increased by subsidence related to the extraction of oil and gas from the delta region.
3 Increased sea level – Sea level has risen by approximately 10 to 15 cm over the past 100 years, and if the predictions related to global warming are correct, a further rise of between 20 to 140 cm can be expected by 2050.
4 Increased rates of coastal erosion – A combination of rising sea levels, together with coastal protection measures at Galveston, Port Arthur and other settlements west of the delta have increased the rate of erosion. Present rates vary between 0.156 and 0.625 hectares per sq km per year, with an average loss of 0.8 per cent per year. The rate can vary enormously, as was demonstrated in September 1979 when hurricane Frederick caused an average 15 m rate of erosion, with some areas experiencing a 40 m rate along parts of the Alabama coastline.

5 Land reclamation – Large areas of the delta and coastal lowlands have been reclaimed, mainly for agriculture, but also in connection with the oil and gas industries. Initially, the agriculture was sugar cane production, but since the 1960s this has been largely, replaced by soybean, rice and crawfish production. This has led to the area of swamp forest declining from 4.9 m hectares to 2.7 m, at a rate of 1.3 per cent per year. The intensive nature of the growth of these products involves high levels of fertiliser, herbicide and pesticide use which can damage sensitive wetland habitats. The expansion of the oil and gas fields involves the construction of 21 m wide canals. These canals have caused a loss of 2.4 per cent of the total wetlands.

Initially, the management of the wetlands was carried out by a variety of federal and state organisations which often resulted in a conflict of

FIGURE 4.5.3 The Louisiana wetlands

interests. The US Corps of Engineers, and the State Department of Natural Resources licensed the dredging of canals, but a Federal authority controlled water pollution through the Water Pollution Control Act (1977) and the Clean Water Act. In the 1980s, the Louisiana Wetlands Authority was created in an attempt to minimise the conflicts. Since its creation the Authority has limited the construction of new canals, introduced water diversion schemes to control the incursion of sea water into brackish marshes, and carried out schemes to protect the coastline adjacent to wetlands. The activities of the Authority have been criticised by a pressure group called the Conservationists Coalition to Restore Coastal

Louisiana. They would like to see more drastic action including:

■ Improved funding for conservation, with finance coming from the oil companies, fishermen and farmers.
■ Control of oil and gas operations, and
■ A limit to the further expansion of the canals.

STUDENT ACTIVITY 4.12

1 Why are wetland areas being lost to economic development?
2 Use Figure 4.5.1 to help you explain the value of wetlands, such as deltas.

4.6 Marine Ecosystems

FIGURE 4.6.1 Ocean ecosystems

Ecosystem	Area (million sq. kms)	Average NPP (g/sq.m/yr)	Total NPP (10^{15} g/yr)
Open ocean	332.0	230	76.2
Upwelling zones	0.4	918	0.4
Continental shelf	26.6	660	17.6
Algal beds and reefs	0.6	2500	1.6
Estuaries	1.4	1500	2.1
Total or average	361.0	271	94.0

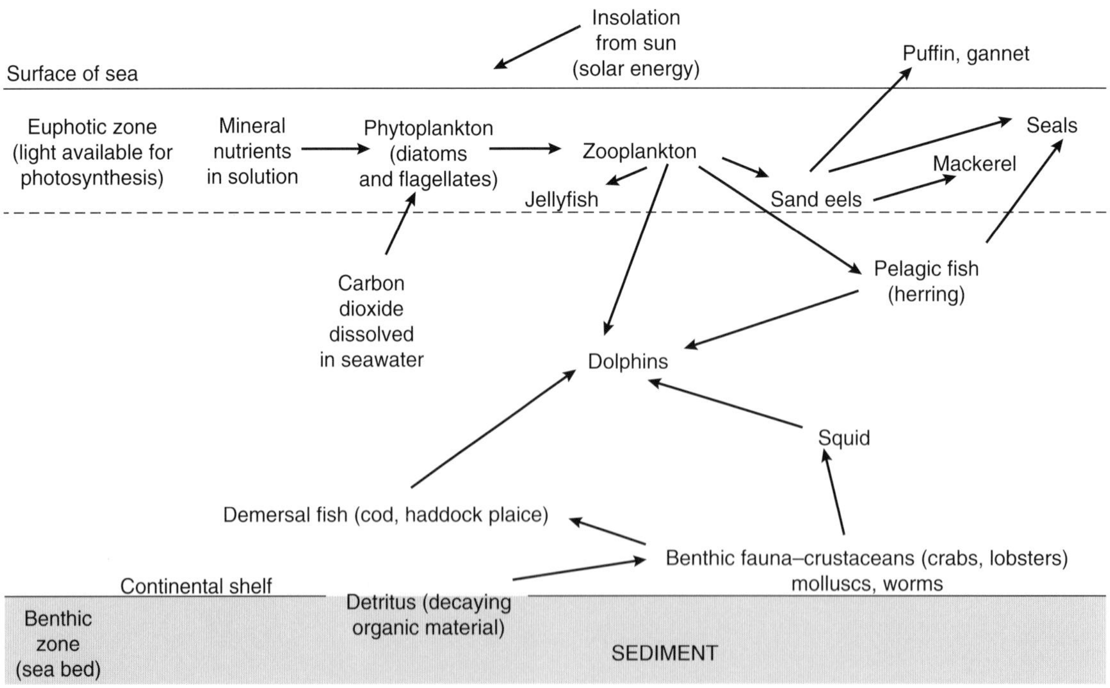

FIGURE 4.6.2 A simplified marine food web

STUDENT ACTIVITY 4.13

Describe and explain the differences in the net primary productivity of the marine ecosystems in Figure 4.6.1

Oceans cover 361 000 000 sq km (71 per cent) of the earth's surface, but account for only 34 per cent of the world's total Net Primary Productivity (NPP). As Figure 4.6.1 illustrates, marine ecosystems vary considerably in their average NPP levels. NPP in the oceans, just as on land, depends upon the ability of the producer (autotroph) organisms to carry out photosynthesis. In the case of the oceans, these organisms are mainly microscopic plants and algae, called **phytoplankton**, and include coccoliths, diatoms, and foraminifera. Phytoplankton occur in the euphotic surface layer of oceans, where light is able to penetrate. The phytoplankton then provide the food for **zooplankton** such as copepods and krill. The plankton are in turn eaten by fish, which because of their ability to swim are also known as the nekton species. Both plankton, and the majority of fish, feed in the pelagic zone which is the main body of the sea. Other organisms feed on the seabed, the benthic zone (Figure 4.6.2).

Sublittoral zone
EUPHOTIC ZONE
NERITIC ZONE
PELAGIC ZONE
Littoral zone
APHOTIC ZONE
Continental shelf
200 m below sea level
Continental slope
ABYSSAL ZONE
3000–6000 m below sea level (trenches to 11 000 m)

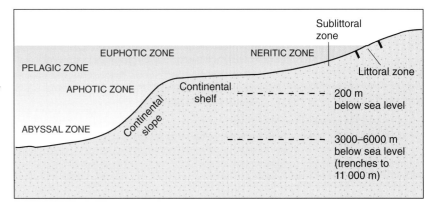

FIGURE 4.6.3 The vertical zones of the oceans

STUDENT ACTIVITY 4.14

Use the information in Figure 4.6.4 to produce a table illustrating the sources and effects of ocean pollution.

Waste not want not
The oceans have been used as a waste dump for centuries. Pollution and over-fishing are pushing the world's oceans towards crisis point
KEY
a Nutrients
Run off approx. 50% sewage, 50% from forestry, farming and other land use
Effects: Decomposing algae depletes water of oxygen, killing marine life.
b Sediments
Erosion from mining, forestry, farming.
Effects: Clogs gills of fish. Smothers and buries coastal ecosystems. Carries toxins/excess nutrients
c Pathogens
Sewage. livestock. Effects: Contaminate coastal swimming areas and seafood, spreading diseases
d Persistent toxins
Industrial discharge waste water from cities; pesticides from farms, forests, home use. Effects: Poisons marine life. Contaminates seafood.
e Oil
46% from cars, heavy machinery, industry, other land-based sources, 32% from oil tanker operations and other shipping. Effects: Low level contamination can kill larvae and cause disease in marine life. Oil slicks kill marine life
f Plastics
Fishing nets; beach litter, wastes from plastics industry and landfills.
Air pollution
Airborne emissions from the land make up 33% by weight of marine pollution. Stratospheric ozone depletion over the poles could affect marine ecosystems
Ozone thinning over poles
Industry b d g e
City e
Rivers a b c d
Increases UV light affecting phytoplankton
Shipping e f
Toxic alert
Offshore industry e
h
g Thermal
Cooling water from power plants and industrial sites.
Effects: Kills off corals and other temperature sensitive sedentary species
h Radioactive isotopes
Discarded submarines and military waste; atmospheric fallout. Effects: Hot spots for radioactivity. Can enter food chain and cause disease in marine life

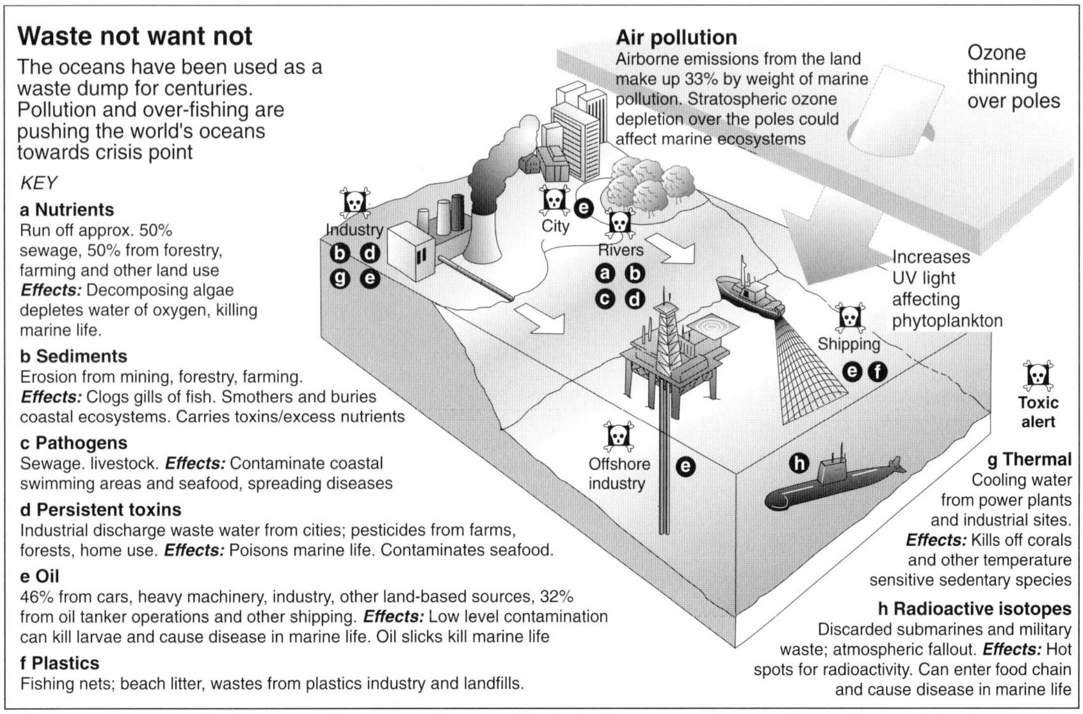

FIGURE 4.6.4 'Waste not, want not' – threats to marine ecosystems

CASE STUDY

The Mediterranean Sea

FIGURE 4.6.5 Annual toxic discharges into the Mediterranean Sea ('000 tonnes)

Area	Nitrates	Phosphates	Mercury	Oil
Alboran basin	25.0	6.6	2.44	1.7
Algerian/Provencal basin	386.8	126.5	33.06	10.0
Balearics	27.2	8.3	2.74	0.6
Tyrrhenian basin	62.3	29.1	10.72	3.0
Adriatic	272.8	85.0	40.58	3.9
Ionian basin	81.5	28.9	11.48	51.0
Aegean Sea	89.7	32.4	14.27	4.1
Antalya/Adana basin	50.6	18.9	7.09	27.0
Levantine basin	55.0	19.5	6.87	13.0
Total Mediterranean	1051.4	355.2	129.25	114.3

The Mediterranean Sea has a 46 000 km coastline, covering 17 countries and containing 130 m people, a figure which is increased by 100 m by summer tourists. Eighty per cent (500 m tonnes per year) of their sewage enters the Sea without being treated. The consequences are polluted beaches, which cause infections including hepatitis and dysentery, and polluted sea food. A report, in 1990, from the UN Environment Programme (UNEP), reported that 93 per cent of shellfish contained more faecal bacteria than the WHO recommended safe level. Annually, large quantities of other pollutants enter the Sea (Figure 4.6.5). Seventy-five per cent of the pollution comes from France, Spain and Italy.

This chemical cocktail is believed to be responsible for many of the recent ecological crises which have included:

1 *Water pollution* – The major effects have included:

■ *Eutrophication* – The accumulation of nitrates and phosphates from agricultural runoff (the rivers of northern Italy add 29 000 cu m of phosphates and 120 000 cu m of nitrates annually), and from sewage have resulted in the growth of algal blooms. The *'red tides'*, which are produced by the build up of dinoflagellates, release toxic chemicals, which affect fish, and hydrogen sulphide. A mucus like foam, secreted by diatoms, may also be produced. This fouls beaches, removes oxygen from the water and kills seabed animals such as heart urchins and shellfish. Red tides have occurred in the Saronikos Gulf in Greece (reducing the number of marine animal species from 170 in 1960, to 30 in 1995) due to pollution from Athens, and the Lac de Tunis in Tunisia where sewage waste from the capital caused one third of the lagoon to be covered by algae. The northern Adriatic Sea, close to Venice, is, however, the worst affected region. The River Po is the main polluter adding 5000 tonnes of phosphates, and 100 000 tonnes of nitrates to the Adriatic each year, ten times the amount discharged 50 years ago. The algae produced may cover up to 50 sq km and contain 50 m tonnes of 'mucus' foam. Each year, in the summer, in an attempt to control the growth of the algae, and reduce the obnoxious smell it produces, the Venice authorities dredge up 1 m tonnes of algae from the lagoon. Its low tidal range, and, during the summer, its warm calm waters, make the pollution problem in the Mediterranean Sea even worse.

■ *The decline of species* – The striped dolphin has been affected by water pollution, particularly by the increase in the levels of PCBs (polychlorinated biphenyls), and other organochlorine compounds, which concentrate in the plankton on which the dolphins feed. Between 1990 and 1992, several thousand were killed by a morbillivirus, which affected their immune system. The concentration of pollutants in the Mediterranean Sea is believed to be linked to two additional factors. In the past 30 years, the increasing number of irrigation schemes in the surrounding countries, especially the Aswan Dam and Lake Nasser on the River Nile have reduced the input of freshwater into the Sea. Highly polluted water from the Black Sea also discharges into the Mediterranean Sea. The renewal of water, from the Atlantic through the Straits of Gibraltar, takes approximately 150 years.

2 *The destruction of habitats and breeding grounds* – The expansion of the tourist industry has been blamed for the decline in the number of logger head turtles, and monk seals (one of the twelve most endangered species in the World). On the beaches of Lagana Bay, on the island of Zakinthos, 500 female logger head turtles normally lay their eggs. These beaches, are now threatened by nearby tourist resorts, as are those of the remaining monk seals.

3 *Overfishing* – There are 500 fish species in the Mediterranean Sea, of which 100 are commercially harvested. Approximately 2 m tonnes of fish are caught each year, but the estimated sustainable yield is between 1.1 and 1.4 m tonnes. Hake, red mullet and sole are particularly at risk. Fishing nets also kill dolphin, as well as damaging posidonia beds ('sea meadows' where fish feed and spawn) and coral reefs.

4 *The spread of 'alien' species* – Over 300 alien (non-native) species of plants and animals have colonised the Sea. The majority have arrived from the Red Sea, via the Suez Canal. In 1985, the tropical green weed *Caulerpa taxifolia* 'escaped' from an aquarium in Monaco and by 1995 it had covered 1500 hectares of the sea bed along 300 km of the coastline. It thrives on sediments rich in accumulated organic material from sewage, and its growth is killing the local posidonia beds.

In 1975, the majority of the countries surrounding the Mediterranean Sea were involved in the production of the *Mediterranean Action Plan* (MEP), which set out specific management aims, and which has been reviewed in both 1985 and 1995.

STUDENT ACTIVITY 4.15

1 Use Figure 4.6.5 to identify the main sources of pollution in the Mediterranean Sea.
2 How have human activities affected this marine ecosystem?
3 Why is it a difficult ecosystem to manage?

CASE STUDY

Coral Reefs

Region	South east Asia	Pacific Ocean	Indian Ocean	Caribbean Sea	Atlantic Ocean	Middle East
% of world's reefs	30	25	24	8	6	6

FIGURE 4.6.6 Distribution of coral reefs

Coral reefs are formed from the skeletons of corals, and other organisms, including molluscs, algae and sponges. It is estimated that coral reefs occur along 600 000 square kilometres of tropical and sub-tropical coast, up to 30 degrees north and south of the Equator.

There are two main types of coral:

1 *Reef building or colonial corals (hermatypic)* – These types of coral live in colonies, and as they grow their skeletons merge together to form reefs. They principally occur in tropical and sub-tropical oceans and seas where the water temperature is above 20°C. Optimum temperatures are between 25° and 30°C. The water needs to be shallow, usually less than 30 m, although some species can grow in water up to 100 m, and free from high sediment and pollution levels. They do not grow on the western sides of continents where cold ocean currents occur, for example, Western Australia. Warm ocean currents, however, for example the Gulf Stream, provide suitable conditions for their growth as far north as Florida and Bermuda.

2 *Ahermatypic or solitary corals* – These types of coral do not build reefs, but are often found in association with colonial corals. They have a wider distribution than colonial corals, being able to live in colder seas, and are found around the British Isles.

Hermatypic corals consist of the coral organism, the polyp, which grows in a symbiotic relationship with a unicellular photosynthetic algae called **zooxanthellae**. The algae is able to use sunlight to carry out photosynthesis, and the host polyp provides the algae with carbon dioxide. The coral polyp is a tiny organism, similar to a sea anemone, with tentacles, which it uses, mainly at night, to capture the zooplankton on which it feeds. As it grows it secretes calcium carbonate (limestone) which forms its skeleton. Rates of growth are usually between 2 to 5 mm per year.

Coral reefs are the most complex and productive marine ecosystems. Although the world average for reef ecosystems is 2500 g/sq.m/yr, a net primary productivity of 7300 g/sq.m/yr has been recorded at Coconut Island, Hawaii. They occur along a coastline as either *fringing reefs* or *barrier reefs*. In the case of islands, particularly volcanic islands in the Pacific and Indian Oceans, which have been subjected to marine erosion forming a sea mount, the reefs may encircle the island, producing an *atoll* which encloses a lagoon. About 1 m plant and animal species are believed to live on coral reefs,

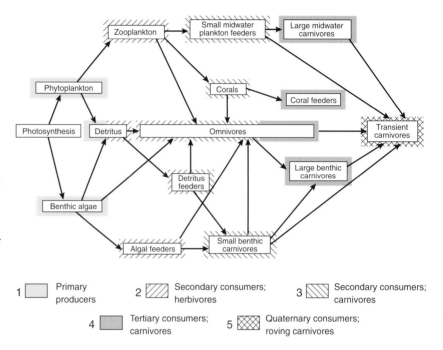

1 Primary producers

2 Secondary consumers; herbivores

3 Secondary consumers; carnivores

4 Tertiary consumers; carnivores

5 Quaternary consumers; roving carnivores

FIGURE 4.6.7 The trophic structure of coral reefs in the Marshall Islands

including over 25 per cent of marine fish. One Tree Reef, in the Great Barrier Reef, Australia has 150 fish species in a 50 square metre area.

Zoning of coral species occurs both vertically and horizontally, reflecting the different wave energy, nutrient and oxygen environments. Coral growth and productivity is higher on the seaward (exposed) side of the reef where zooplankton, oxygen and nutrient levels are higher. The deeper areas of the seaward reef are usually formed from seabed reef limestone, consisting of the dead remains of coral, calcareous algae and animal skeletons. Above this zone calcareous algae may grow, with the main or head coral zone of large, long lived corals just below the low water level. The leeward or inner reef is less productive. As the coral reef becomes larger it helps to absorb wave energy, and helps to protect the coastline. The lower energy wave conditions created allow sea grasses to colonise these areas. The sea grass then traps sediment, and nutrients, providing even more favourable conditions which allow mangroves to succeed the sea grasses.

The World Conservation Union (IUCN) has estimated that 10 per cent of the world's coral reefs have been degraded beyond recovery, with significant degradation being recorded in 93 out of 109 countries with coral reefs. Over the next 20 years, a further 30 per cent are expected to be

FIGURE 4.6.8 Coral reef and mangrove habitats

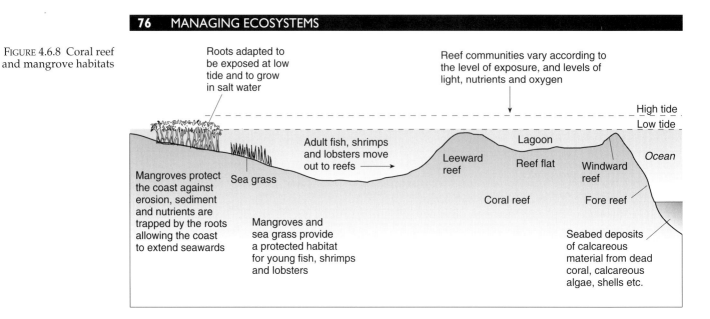

severely degraded. South East Asia's are the most species rich, and the most threatened, with 80 per cent. Reefs are under threat from a variety of human and natural processes:

1 Overfishing – The natural productivity and diversity of the reefs has resulted in them becoming important fishing areas. The fish caught include commercial species, such as emperors, groupers, snappers and jacks, as well as a wide range of ornamental or aquarium species caught live for export. Also caught are green turtles, oysters, giant clams and spiny lobsters. A variety of fishing methods are used including trawls, drive-in nets, spear guns, poisons (cyanide, chlorine, bleach and DDT), and even explosives.

2 Coral Mining – On many islands, especially atolls, coral may be the only available building stone. In the Maldives in the Indian Ocean, for example, it has been estimated that 111 000 cu m of coral has been mined over 20 years.

3 Tourism – Coral reefs are very attractive areas to visit, but, unfortunately, they are very sensitive to change. Tourists visiting reefs usually require first class reefs, together with excellent visitor accommodation and facilities. This may immediately produce a conflict of interest. The reefs may be damaged directly, as a result of the

construction of hotels etc., or indirectly from the increased sediment, if mangroves or other vegetated areas are destroyed during the construction process. A further problem is caused by sewage waste from the urban areas and nitrate rich agricultural run off. In the 1970s, at Kaneohe Bay in Hawaii, nearly all the coral was destroyed by sewage waste. In 1978, the sewage outfall was diverted, and by 1985 the reefs were being recolonised. Other indirect consequences of tourism include pollution from fuel sources, and the water disturbance caused by motor boats. Direct contact damage to the reefs is caused through reef walking, coral collecting for souvenirs, and boat anchors. The level of damage is often closely related to the frequency of visits to the reef. Reefs at the John Pennekamp National Park in Florida are visited 150 000 times per year.

4 El Nino – In 1979–80, 1982–83, and 1986–88 severe 'bleaching' of coral reefs was recorded. This occurs when the symbiotic relationship between the coral hosts and zooxanthellae is disrupted, resulting in the ejection of the zooxanthellae allowing the white skeleton of the coral to be seen. It is believed that the cause is an increase in sea temperature. Due either to the El Nino effect, when sea levels are lowered in parts of the Pacific Ocean, and the cold

FIGURE 4.6.9 The management of the major problems affecting coral reefs

Overfishing	Coral mining	Tourism
■ Elimination of damaging fishing methods ■ Introduction of fisheries reserves ■ Mariculture (farming) of commercial reef species ■ Import and export controls on exotic species through CITES (Convention on International Trade in Endangered Species)	■ Regulation of coral mining e.g. it was made illegal in 1983 in Sri Lanka	■ Creation of protected areas ■ Development of eco-tourism ■ Integrated Coastal Zone Management

temperatures of parts of the Peru Current are replaced by warmer conditions, or due to global warming. In the 1990s, average summer sea temperatures in the Caribbean Sea have been 1° to 3°C higher than normal. Other causes, are related to pollution and increased sediment levels.

5 Biological problems – Many reefs, particularly in the South Pacific, have been severely affected by either the crown of thorns starfish or coralline lethal orange disease.

6 Rising sea levels – The predicted rise in sea level of 4 to 5 mm per year over the next 50 to 100 years will affect the reefs. If the rise is slow active reefs should be able to maintain their growth rates.

Management

Three thousand marine protected areas, as defined by the IUCN, have been created, of which 400 (13 per cent) include coral reefs. The principal aims of these areas are to maintain the natural habitats, to maintain the biodiversity, to protect the breeding populations of the key commercial species, and to produce a management plan consisting of specific use zones to minimise conflict. Many of the management plans are based on the concept of *integrated coastal management*, reflecting the need to include coastal areas, which include pollution sources such as urban and agricultural areas.

CASE STUDY

Problems and Management of Coral Reefs – The Great Barrier Reef Marine Protection Area (GBRMPA) of Australia

The GBRMPA in Queensland, Australia, was created in 1970. It covers an area of 11 800 sq km of the Great Barrier Reef, is 2000 km in length, and is divided into 5 zones. Its 2500 individual reefs have many of the problems already mentioned above.

One particular problem has been the large increase in the number of the crown of thorns starfish (*Acanthaster planc.*). The problem was first noticed in the 1960s, and it is estimated that the starfish, by eating the coral polyps, has destroyed 14 per cent of the reefs in the GBRMPA. A single starfish may consume 6 sq m of coral a year. The dead corals are then usually colonised by algae, and sea urchins. The increase may be due to a natural cycle. Other explanations blame human activities, including an increase in the growth of algae, due to agricultural and sewage nutrient discharges from the land, which starfish larvae then feed on, and the removal of starfish predators through overfishing.

The expansion of tourist facilities along the Queensland coast is also a threat to the reefs. The development of coastal resorts, at various towns including Cairns and Port Douglas, has often involved the destruction of mangroves. Mangrove forests are vital to the reefs in trapping sediment and mineral nutrients, and acting as a 'nursery' for young fish. Urbanisation has also involved the construction of new roads, frequently resulting in a twenty fold increase in sediment runoff. The increasing permanent and tourist population has led to problems, as untreated or partially treated sewage, rich in nitrates and phosphates, is discharged into local rivers and the Pacific Ocean. In order to protect the natural habitats of the Great Barrier Reef, and to regulate the location of the economically important tourist activities, the GBRMPA has produced a management plan, based on the concept of the 'biosphere reserve', dividing the area into five types of user zone (Figure 4.6.10).

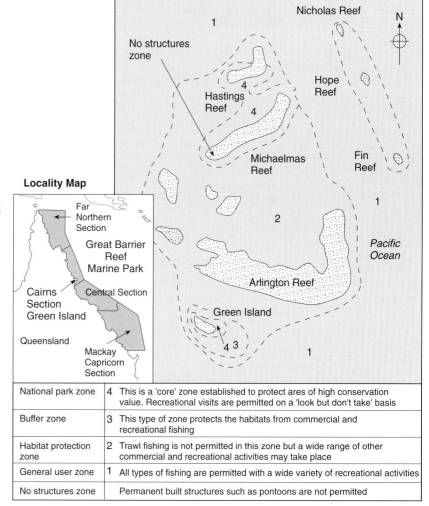

National park zone	4	This is a 'core' zone established to protect ares of high conservation value. Recreational visits are permitted on a 'look but don't take' basis
Buffer zone	3	This type of zone protects the habitats from commercial and recreational fishing
Habitat protection zone	2	Trawl fishing is not permitted in this zone but a wide range of other commercial and recreational activities may take place
General user zone	1	All types of fishing are permitted with a wide variety of recreational activities
No structures zone		Permanent built structures such as pontoons are not permitted

FIGURE 4.6.10 The management zones of the Great Barrier Reef

STUDENT ACTIVITY 4.16

1 Identify the major threats facing coral reef ecosystems from (i) natural factors and (ii) human activities.

2 What solutions have been used to manage these problems?

5
ECOSYSTEMS OF THE
BRITISH ISLES

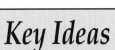

Key Ideas

■ Most of Britain is covered by plagioclimax habitats, which show the influence of human activities.

■ Although the area covered by Britain's woodlands has increased in recent years, most of the new woodlands are large coniferous plantations.

■ Many areas of upland heath are protected by occurring within national parks. Lowland heath, however, has seen a drastic decrease in its area.

■ Many peatlands are being lost, with lowland peatlands converted to agriculture, and upland areas converted to forestry.

■ Agricultural 'improvement' has altered most of Britain's grasslands. Grants are now available to manage grasslands in a more 'traditional' way.

■ Many rivers are being affected by surface water and ground water abstraction, and the effects of pollution from domestic, agricultural and industrial sources.

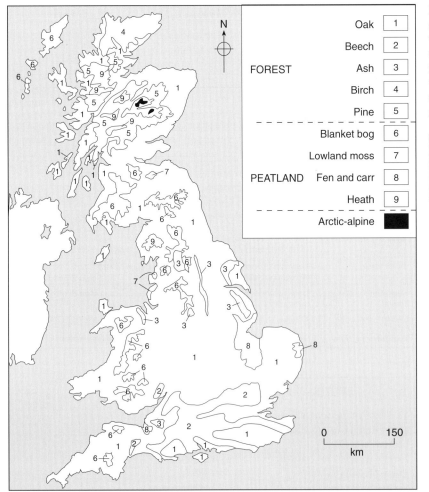

	FOREST	Oak	1
		Beech	2
		Ash	3
		Birch	4
		Pine	5
	PEATLAND	Blanket bog	6
		Lowland moss	7
		Fen and carr	8
		Heath	9
		Arctic-alpine	■

Following several thousand years of human activities, very few areas of 'natural climax' vegetation remain in Britain. A theoretical distribution of the climax communities is illustrated in Figure 5.0.1. This chapter investigates some of the ways in which selected British ecosystems are being subject to change, and how change may be managed.

STUDENT ACTIVITY 5.I

Describe and explain the theoretical distribution of climax vegetation shown on Figure 5.0.1

FIGURE 5.0.1 Climatic climax communities of Britain

5.1 Woodlands

Woodland types in England and Wales (thousand hectares)				Woodland Ownership (thousand hectares)						
Date	**Deciduous**	**Mixed**	**Coniferous**		**Forestry Commission**			**Private Woodland**		
1947	851	106	104	Deciduous	38	7	6	401	56	84
1969	712	149	329	Conifers	177	118	508	207	53	458
1992	542	114	555							

Woodland types in England (1996)			Causes of forest loss in England since 1930	
Woodland Type	**Area (ha)**	**Percentage**	**Cause**	**Area Lost (ha)**
Plantation	236 842	45	Agricultural expansion	20 304
Ancient	200 000	38	Urban development	6498
Semi-natural	89 474	17	Mineral extraction	1965

FIGURE 5.1.1 Woodland types, ownership, and loss

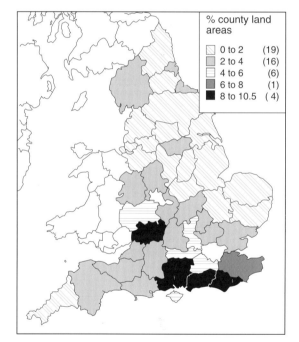

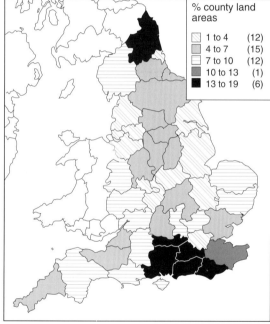

FIGURE 5.1.2 Areas of woodland in England as a percentage of county land area: (a) ancient woodland cover (b) total woodland cover

In Britain, only 9 per cent of the land surface is wooded, compared to the European Union average of 29 per cent. British woodlands are a mixture of ancient woodland (which has been in existence since at least 1600 AD), recent semi-natural woodland, if they are the result of the 'natural' colonisation of land, or if planted by humans, plantation woodlands. In England, woodland covers 7.5 per cent of its area, a figure which has increased, mainly due to large scale coniferous planting, from the 4 per cent recorded in 1900. The county variations in ancient and total woodland cover are shown in Figure 5.1.2.

British woodlands face threats from a variety of sources, including:

- total clearance for other uses
- woodland fragmentation
- lack of suitable management
- overgrazing
- the introduction of alien (non-native) species
- acid rain and other types of pollution, and
- recreational uses.

Since 1930, 28 767 hectares (7 per cent) of English ancient woodland have been lost, 20 304 to agriculture, 6498 to urban development, and 1965 to mineral extraction, and 39 per cent has been replanted.

Woodland may be managed for three main uses:

1 Commercial uses including timber production, game (deer and pheasant) management and stock grazing.
2 Leisure uses such as camping, cycle trails and orienteering, and the
3 The conservation of habitats and landscape.
The Forestry Commission is the major agency in woodland management, owning in 1996

approximately 40 per cent (1 187 711 hectares) of Britain's woodlands. It was established, in 1919, after World War 1 revealed the inadequate extent of Britain's woodlands. By 1957 it owned 500 000 hectares. The functions of the Forestry Commission are divided between the *Forestry Authority* (which administers grants such as the Woodland Grant Scheme, the Farm Woodland Premium Scheme and the Community Woodland Supplement), and *Forestry Enterprise*, which is responsible for the day to day management of the forests. In December 1998 the Labour Government announced plans to spend approximately £40 million per year planting new trees, reversing the previous Conservative policy which saw 124 918 ha of Forestry Commission woodland sold to private businesses between 1981 and 1996.

FIGURE 5.1.3

Britain 'failing its forests'

Britain is fourth from bottom for forestry management among European countries according to the first detailed survey on the subject, devised by the Worldwide Fund for Nature (WWF).

'The UK has virtually no natural forests left, and some ecosystem types have entirely disappeared. Forest cover is low and most British "forests" are actually plantations' says the WWF report. 'Despite widespread loss, only 2.5 per cent of the remaining area is under strict protection.'

The criteria the WWF used were levels of pollution, the amount of protected forest area, the standards of production and the national environmental, social and cultural policies applied to forests. Britain is dragged down the league table by the worst score in Europe for pollution, measured by annual per capita emissions of carbon dioxide, sulphur, nitrogen and volatile organic compounds.

Source *Guardian* 27 May 1998

FIGURE 5.1.4 Deciduous woodland food web

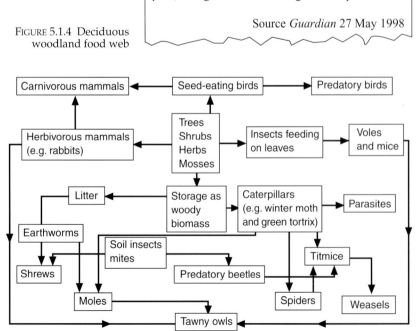

STUDENT ACTIVITY 5.2

Refer to Figures 5.1.1, 5.1.2 and 5.1.3, and analyse the changes in British woodlands since 1930.

Broadleaved or Deciduous Woodlands

Deciduous trees are those that lose their leaves in winter in response to a reduction in available soil moisture, due to lower temperatures, and to lower light levels. The main native broadleaved trees are oaks, ash, beech and birch, non-native trees include the sycamore, sweet chestnut and horse chestnut. The average net primary productivity (NPP) of temperate deciduous woodlands is 1200 g/sq.m/yr, with a range from 600 to 2500 g/sq.m/yr. In Britain, NPP is limited by the seasonal nature of the climate, with most plant growth occurring in spring and summer when there are higher light levels, temperatures above 6°C, and soil moisture is more available.

Many animals migrate, are dormant, or in hibernation during the winter months, limiting energy flow through the system. In the summer months, NPP and animal populations increase, as does the rate of decomposition of leaf litter. Deciduous trees, particularly oaks, are associated with a large number of animal species, particularly of insects and birds, producing complex food webs.

Oak woods may represent the climax vegetation of several types of prisere. Pedunculate oak occurs in lowland areas, up to 300 metres, with sessile oak growing at higher altitudes, up to 450 metres. Oaks normally occur on *brown forest earth* soils. These soils have a deep, nutrient rich A horizon, formed by the rapid decomposition of the leaf litter by a very diverse soil fauna. On chalk areas, such as the Chilterns and North and South Downs, where there are well drained *rendzina* soils, beech is often the dominant type of tree. On the Carboniferous Limestone of the Pennines, and Jurassic Limestone of the North York Moors ash is frequently dominant. Silver birch and downy birch are pioneer species, with silver birch being common on drier soils, and downy birch on wetter and more exposed sites.

Oak woods, particularly, have a distinctive vertical structure consisting of four layers. These comprise a tree layer of oaks, a shrub layer composed, for example, of hazel, holly and hornbeam, an herb layer, and a ground layer mainly of grasses. The herb layer varies with the amount of available light. In early spring, before the trees are

STUDENT ACTIVITY 5.3

Use the information in Figure 5.1.4 to produce a table illustrating the producers, and primary, secondary and tertiary consumers of this oak woodland ecosystem.

FIGURE 5.1.5 Dell Woods and the Ancient Caledonian Forest

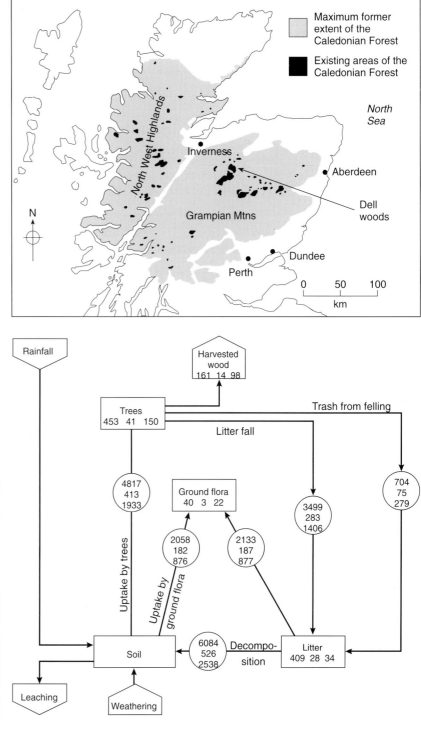

in leaf, light demanding species such as lesser celandine, dog's mercury and wood anemone flower. These are followed by more shade tolerant species including bluebells, yellow wood sage, red campion, rosebay willow herb, sanicle and foxgloves.

Coniferous Woods

In Britain toady, coniferous woodlands are dominated by non-native species, including Sitka spruce and Norway spruce, occurring in large scale plantations. Originally, Scots pine, one of Britain's three native conifers (the other two being juniper and yew), covered a large part of northern Britain. In Scotland, it has been estimated that it once covered 20 per cent (1 500 000 hectares) of the surface, and formed the Caledonian Forest. The Caledonian Forest is now restricted to, approximately, 12 000 hectares of the Scottish Highlands (1 per cent of Scotland's area) (Figure 5.1.5). In 1978, the Forestry Commission introduced the *Native Pinewood Grant Scheme*, covering a large area of the former range of the Scots pine in the Scottish Highlands, to increase the planted area of the tree.

FIGURE 5.1.6 The nutrient cycle of a 55 year old managed coniferous (Scots pine) forest. Figures in circles show flows of nitrogen, phosphorous and potassium totalled over the 55 years of growth; figures in boxes show the total amounts retained at the end of the period

STUDENT ACTIVITY 5.4

1 Use the information in Figure 5.1.6 to analyse the movement of nutrients in this commercial plantation coniferous forest ecosystem.
2 What are the implications of these nutrient flows for the commercial management of the forest?

CASE STUDY

Dell Woods

Dell Woods, located east of Aviemore, is one of only 35 woods in Scotland where the Scots pine grows naturally. It is part of the Abernethy forest, the most extensive single area of Scots pine left in Britain, and a remnant of the formerly far more extensive Caledonian Forest. Pollen analysis of the site has shown that Scots pine have occupied the area for the last 8000 years.

On average, the pine has a higher level of net primary productivity (1300 g/sq.m/yr) than deciduous trees (1200 g/sq.m/yr). This is because being evergreen it can photosynthesise throughout a longer period of the year, extending its growing season. Pine trees produce large amounts of leaf litter, which accumulates on the ground surface, as the rate of decomposition is lower than in deciduous forests. This is partly due to the nature of the pine needles, and to the acidic conditions which restrict the number of organisms that decompose organic matter. Scots pine is similar to other conifers in that it occurs on *podsols*. Podsols have a low nutrient status due to the high level of leaching, and the low input of nutrients from the vegetation. This has the effect of restricting the growth of deciduous trees with their higher nutrient demand. At Dell Woods, Scots pine may reach 20 m, and obtain nutrients from a large area by producing shallow spreading roots. Birch trees, and the evergreen shrub juniper also occur, together with ling (common heather) and blaeberry.

A stunted form of Scots pine, reaching 4 to 5 m, has developed on the wetter bog areas. Over 70 species of birds are found in the woods, including the rare Scottish crossbill which feeds on the typical 3000 pine cones produced annually by each tree. Insects include the long horn beetle and the poplar hawk moth. Mammals including the rare wildcat, pine marten and red squirrel, together with roe and red deer occur in the reserve. One of the management aims is to control the level of browsing, by the deer, through selective culling and tree protection schemes. Non-native trees are also being cleared and replaced with Scots pine and birch.

Coniferous Afforestation

In 1996, coniferous forest formed approximately 70 per cent of the total woodland of Britain, most of which was planted forest. Initially, the majority of coniferous plantations were planted, and owned by the Forestry Commission, but the privatisation policy operated since 1989 has resulted in an approximately 50:50 split between the Forestry Commission and private owners.

Sitka spruce is the most commonly planted tree (Figure 5.1.7). It is adaptable, being able to be planted up to altitudes of 600 m, and to tolerate exposed sites with strong winds and which receive high rainfall totals. The native Scots pine, in contrast, prefers well drained, dry sandy soils.

FIGURE 5.1.7 Conifer types planted in Britain

Type of Conifer	Percentage
Sitka spruce	40
Scots pine	18
European and Japanese larches	11
Norway spruce	9
Douglas fir	4
Others	18

Early plantations were criticised for their uniform planting in rows, often of only one species, usually Sitka spruce, and with little regard for the effect on the landscape or wildlife. Modern plantations are designed more sensitively. The Royal Society for the Protection of Birds recommend that new plantations should be planted:

■ away from sensitive wildlife areas,
■ near to urban areas where they can also be used for recreation,
■ on land which has been taken out of agricultural use, and should

■ contain both broadleaved and coniferous species. They also recommend that existing plantations should be reshaped to enhance the landscape, and that forests planted on important habitats, such as lowland heath, should be removed.

The expansion of coniferous softwoods, rather than deciduous hardwoods reflects several factors. Firstly, Britain uses approximately ten times more softwood than hardwood. Sitka spruce, especially, provides suitable timber for producing both pulp (which is then made into paper), and chipboard. Secondly, conifers grow more quickly than broadleaved trees, and can be harvested economically after 50 years. Thirdly, conifers are more able to grow on exposed sites with poor soil conditions. The extension of coniferous plantations has provided much needed employment, especially in upland areas where hill sheep farming is often the major economic activity. They are also used for a variety of recreational activities. Apart from their effect upon the landscape, and the loss of native habitats and wildlife, concern has been expressed about their effect on local rivers and lakes. The ploughing and drainage of the land prior to planting, causes increased surface runoff and increased sediment levels in rivers. Pesticides, herbicides and fertilisers used in the plantations are frequently carried into rivers and lakes by runoff and throughflow. Conifers have the effect of lowering the pH of the leaf litter, and soil, and consequently produce acidic runoff, which in turn can lead to the acidification of rivers and lakes. This problem is frequently compounded by acid rain, and may require the water to be treated by adding lime to neutralise the acidity as has happened at Loch Fleet.

CASE STUDY

New Forest

The New Forest, located in Hampshire, is the largest English forest. In 1992 it was designated the New Forest Heritage Area (NFHA), with a special status similar to a national park, and its area was enlarged to 57 783 hectares. Fifty-four per cent of the NFHA is used for agriculture and urban development. The remainder, 72 per cent of which is owned by the Forestry Commission, is divided into the 'Enclosures' (15 per cent), and the 'Open Forests' (31 per cent).

1 The *Enclosures* are the main areas of timber production, with conifers covering 57 per cent of their area. In 1995–96 they produced 31 000 cu m of softwood timber. The conifers are initially planted two metres apart at a density of 2 300 trees per hectare. After 20 years, they are thinned out every five years, and are harvested between 45 and 70 years after planting. Selective regeneration felling occurs where necessary. Broadleaved trees cover 39 per cent (3 389 hectares) of the Enclosures, and in 1995–96 produced 4 000 cu m of timber. They are planted at the same density as the conifers, but after 30 years are thinned every 10 years, with regeneration felling occurring after 200 years.

2 The *Open Forest* contains a very diverse mosaic of habitats. Lowland heath, occurring on the podsolic soils of the plateau gravels in the north and the Barton Sands and Headon Beds in the south, is the dominant habitat covering 31 per cent of the area (Figure 5.1.9). Wet heath and acid grasslands are found along the river valleys, especially in the north. In the south, the wider more open valleys often produce valley bog communities. The central area with its mixture of clays and sands often has a brown forest earth supporting oak and beech woods. This broadleaved woodland forms the Ancient and Ornamental Woodlands, designated by the New Forest Act of 1877. Early management of the trees often consisted of pollarding, where the top of the tree was removed to encourage the growth of several new shoots. This is similar to coppicing, which involves cutting the tree down to a stump, from which new shoots will

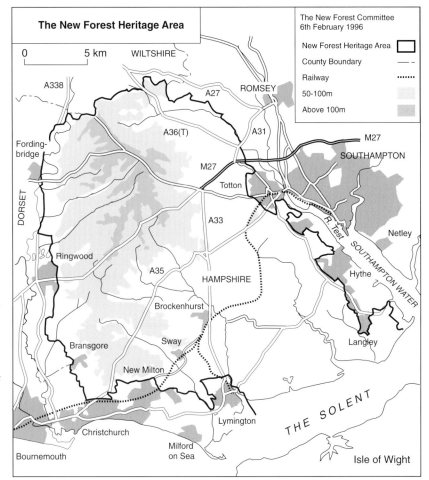

FIGURE 5.1.8 The location of the New Forest Heritage Area

grow. In the New Forest, the many grazing animals would have quickly eaten the coppice shoots. In many areas of the NFHA there is a close correlation between habitat type and landform (Figure 5.1.10). The importance of the variety of habitats in the New Forest, and the need for their protection, has been recognised by considerable legislation (Figure 5.1.11). The NFHA is also an important producer of timber, provides grazing for ponies, sheep and cattle, and attracts 8 m visitors per annum. These uses may conflict and require careful management.

FIGURE 5.1.9 New Forest commercial tree types and habitats

Tree type	Percentage	Tree type	Percentage	Open Forest Habitats	Area (ha)	Percentage
Scots pine	20	Pure oak	17	Calluna heathland	5539	31
Corsican pine	13	Mixed oak/beech	13	Acid grasslands	4793	27
Douglas fir	12	Pure beech	4	Oak/beech woodlands	3540	20
Spruce	5	Other	2	Valley bogs/wet heath	2597	14
Larch	2			Scots pine	434	2
Other	2			Forest lawn grasslands	324	2
				Other	728	4
		Other woodland	10	Total	18511	100

FIGURE 5.1.10 New Forest
habitats and landforms

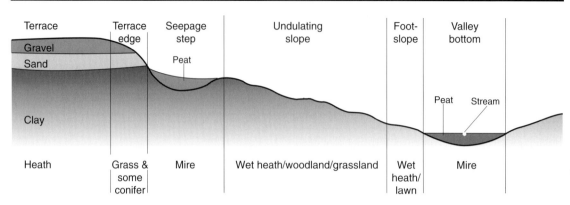

The NFHA is managed by the New Forest Committee, an independent non-statutory body composed of representatives from the various agencies with an interest in the New Forest. These include the Forestry Commission, English Nature, the Countryside Commission, the Verderers of the New Forest, and local councils.

Apart from the management of the coniferous and broadleaved woodlands, other general management issues include:

FIGURE 5.1.11 New Forest
conservation

Date	Legislation
1877	New Forest Act
1949	New Forest Act
1964	New Forest Act
1967	Forestry Act
1967	Designation as part of the South Hampshire Coast Area of Outstanding Natural Beauty
1969	Designation as a National Nature Reserve
1972	Designation as a Site of Special Scientific Interest (SSSI)
1991	National Parks Review Panel recommended its recognition as a National Park
1992	Designation as the New Forest Heritage Area (NFHA) with a status similar to a National Park
1993	Designation as a RAMSAR site, a Wetland of International Importance
1993	Designation as a Special Protection Area (SPA) under the EU Wild Birds Directive
1995	Proposed designation as a Special Area of Conservation (SAC)
1998	Proposed designation as a national park rejected by the Countryside Commission

■ *The need to maintain the quality of the areas of lowland heath.* The heath areas are managed by cutting and burning as a means of controlling the growth of scrub vegetation. Gorse is cut or burnt on a 12 year cycle, which increases to 25 years for heather.
■ *The regulation of grazing.* The three hundred Commoners, people who own or occupy a piece of land in the New Forest, have the right to graze animals in the Open Forest. In 1994 the animals included 4112 ponies, 2688 cattle, 89 pigs, 195 donkeys and 185 sheep! The Forest also contains

several herds of fallow and red deer. The management of grazing, the animals, and the conservation of the Open Forest is traditionally by the Verderers Court, which was set up by the 1877 New Forest Act.
■ *The management of habitat erosion due to the increasing pressure from recreational activities.* 'A Framework for Recreation' published by the Forestry Commission in 1997, identified several locations where it occurs:

1 along footpaths adjacent to car parks,
2 along bridleways and other locations, due to their use for horse riding, trial motorcycles, and 4×4 motor vehicles, and
3 at 18 camp sites with a total of 4950 tent pitches.

Habitat erosion is being controlled with a programme of vegetation restoration, and the number of tent pitches is being decreased. The Forest has also been divided into four recreational zones, based on their susceptibility to erosion from recreational use, and to which different management policies can be applied:

1 the enclosed timber growing woodlands are the most robust areas, and can accommodate a higher level of recreational use,
2 the reseeded 'open grasslands or lawns' are believed to be able to withstand higher levels of use,
3 the heathlands and other semi-natural open habitats are more sensitive and need careful management, and
4 the unenclosed broadleaved woodlands, including the riverside woodlands, are the least robust areas, and the least suited to recreational use.

STUDENT ACTIVITY 5.5

1 Why has the New Forest such a wide range of habitats?
2 How have the habitats been protected?
3 Why do you think that the Countryside Commission decided not to designate the New Forest a national park?
4 Outline a management plan for the New Forest, which identifies:
■ the major issues, and
■ possible management solutions.

Community Forests and the National Forest

In 1987, the Countryside Commission, in *'Forestry in the countryside'*, outlined the need for the development of new multipurpose areas of forest on the edges of cities. It suggested the creation of two types of forest. Firstly, community forests consisting of a network of woodlands around the major cities, and secondly, the National Forest, a major forest area to be located in the English midlands. In England, since 1990, the Countryside Commission and the Forestry Commission have created twelve Community Forests (Figure 5.1.12).

The aim is to increase the tree cover in the Community Forest areas to 30 per cent of the land area. The forests are to improve the landscape, and for commercial, educational, recreational and conservation uses. In 1997, they ranged in size from 100 to over 750 sq km, and covered a total area of 4700 sq km.

In 1990 the then Conservative Government announced the creation of the National Forest, designated to cover 518 sq km and located to the north-west of Leicester. It will include the existing Needwood and Charnwood forests, together with some of the derelict mining areas of the Leicestershire coalfield, which are to be reclaimed and planted mainly with broadleaved trees including oak, beech, ash and willow. In 1994 the National Forest Company was created with initial government funding of £2 m a year.

FIGURE 5.1.12
Community Forests and the National Forest

STUDENT ACTIVITY 5.6

Why has it been necessary to create the National Forest and Community Forests?

5.2 Grasslands

It is easy to imagine that the large areas of grassland found in Britain today are the result of natural processes. They are, however, the product of 7000 years of deforestation.

There are a very large number of different species of grasses and sedges, enabling them to colonise a wide variety of habitats. Grassland habitats may be classified by their soil pH, into *acid* (*calcifuge*) with a pH below 5.5, *neutral* with a pH of between 5.5 and 7, and *calcareous* (pH above 7).

The majority of grasslands are used for some

type of agriculture with, on the acidic grasslands, hill sheep farming dominating in the uplands, and beef and dairy cattle in the lowlands. Inevitably, most of these grasslands have been 'improved' by the addition of fertilisers and herbicides, and by drainage. Many of the improved grasslands have been ploughed and reseeded with quick growing perennial grasses, such as common rye grass. These grasslands have a low species diversity, with very few herb species, compared with the 'unimproved' grasslands.

CASE STUDY

The Yorkshire Dales National Park

Over 57 per cent of the land surface of the Yorkshire Dales National Park (YDNP) is covered by grassland (Figure 5.2.1). Neutral grasslands cover the largest area, and are mainly found along the floodplains and lower slopes of the major valleys, especially Wensleydale, the Swale, the Wharfe, and the Ribble. Most of these areas are improved pasture, but there are many areas of unimproved

hay meadows which have a particularly diverse range of species. At higher altitudes rough pasture occurs and is dominated by acidic grasslands consisting of mat grass, with wavy hair grass on the exposed gritstones, and heath rush in the wetter areas. Where there is a transition to bog communities, soft rush and tufted hair grass become more common.

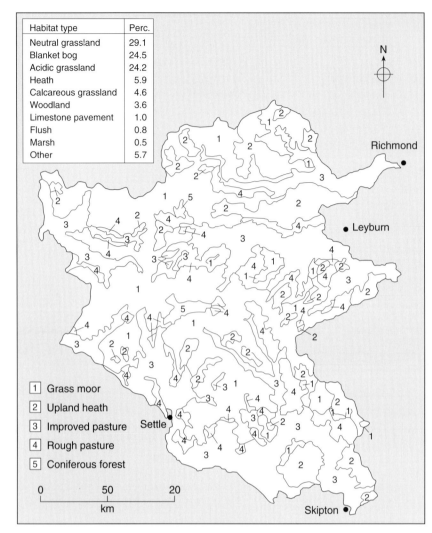

Habitat type	Perc.
Neutral grassland	29.1
Blanket bog	24.5
Acidic grassland	24.2
Heath	5.9
Calcareous grassland	4.6
Woodland	3.6
Limestone pavement	1.0
Flush	0.8
Marsh	0.5
Other	5.7

1. Grass moor
2. Upland heath
3. Improved pasture
4. Rough pasture
5. Coniferous forest

0   50   20
km

Figure 5.2.1 Habitats of the Yorkshire Dales National Park

■ the application of fertilisers, herbicides, and pesticides,
■ to enlarge fields by removing stone walls or hedges, or
■ to drain the upper pastures and areas of rough grazing.

All of these will have an effect upon both the landscape and the wildlife of the Park. Farmers are being encouraged to use traditional farming practices through a variety of schemes providing environmental grants:

1 *Pennine Dales Environmentally Sensitive Area (ESA)* – Several of the dales in the YDNP, including Swaledale, Wharfedale and Wensleydale, are included within this ESA, which is financed by the Ministry of Agriculture, Fisheries and Food (MAFF). Through it farmers enter into 10 year agreements with MAFF to adopt agricultural practices which help to protect and enhance the environment. Some of the practices in the Pennine Dales include improving herb rich meadows by reducing stocking levels and restricting inorganic fertiliser application, creating or improving broadleaf woodlands, and maintaining or extending stone walls. In return they receive various grants, for example, in 1997 farmers could obtain £240 per hectare for herb rich meadows and a walling renovation grant of £14 per metre.
2 *The Countryside Stewardship Scheme*, originally implemented by the Countryside Commission but now by MAFF, which provides grants for maintaining habitats such as the limestone grasslands.
3 *The Wildlife Enhancement Scheme*, implemented by English Nature, and available to those farmers who farm the 50 Sites of Special Scientific Interest (SSSI), covering 15 per cent of the Park.

Two of the SSSIs, Ingleborough and Malham Tarn, also have National Nature Reserve status. Both of the National Nature Reserves, together with 21 hay meadows have been proposed as *Special Areas of Conservation*. In 1997, the *Yorkshire Dales Millennium Trust* was established with a grant of £4 m from the Millennium Commission. For each £100 000 raised by the Trust, £2 m will be provided by the Commission, totalling £8 m over four years. Grants from the Trust will be used for a variety of environmental and community projects. Between 1997 and 2001, it is hoped that 40 new Millennium Woods, of ash, oak and hazel, will be created, together with the restoration of 160 hectares of old woodland. Five new *Nature Conservation Areas* are also to be created, and 14 other habitats will be established by improving riverbanks.

In order to improve the drainage of these grasslands many farmers have built drainage gullies, a practice known as moorland gripping. In the 1970s, gripping covered an area of 865 sq km, which by the 1980s had increased by 48 per cent to 1280 sq km. Apart from the effect on the moorland habitat, it is believed that moorland gripping has contributed to the increased discharge, and frequency of flooding of the River Ure at Boroughbridge and the River Ouse at York.

The calcareous (calcicole) grasslands, consisting of grasses such as blue moor grass, occur in the south where they are associated with the thin rendzina soils developed on the Carboniferous Great Scar Limestone. The marshy grasslands of soft rush or sharp-flowered rush marsh, although widespread, cover only a small total area being found near to streams, in wet hollows, and on poorly drained level areas.

Although the Yorkshire Dales is designated as a *national* park, over 96 per cent of its area is privately owned, mainly by farmers. The majority are either hill sheep or dairy farmers, and it is in their interests to farm profitably. Farming in areas such as the Yorkshire Dales is often marginal, and the Park is designated as a Less Favourable Area. Farmers may need to improve their land through:

STUDENT ACTIVITY 5.7

1 To what extent have the habitats of the YDNP been affected by human activities?
2 How are the landscapes and wildlife of the park protected?

CASE STUDY

Soil Erosion on Chalk Downlands

Chalk grasslands or downlands are under considerable pressure, with 80 per cent of their area being lost, mainly to agriculture, since 1940. Initially, they were mainly forested, usually by beech, but the clearance of the woodlands has a long history, commencing 7000 years ago in the Neolithic Age. Today, apart from protected reserves, unimproved chalk grasslands are largely restricted to those areas, for example scarp slopes, which are too steep for agriculture. In the Middle Ages, it was usual for sheep to be grazed on the upper downland slopes, and for wheat to be grown on the valley bottoms. The gradual intensification of farming, combined with improvements in technology has resulted in arable farming extending onto the steeper slopes. This trend increased during, and after World War II, and now slopes up to 25 degrees are ploughed. Initially, this was for spring sown wheat and barley, retaining the previous year's stubble over the winter. Particularly since the 1970s, the trend has been one of the autumn sowing of winter cereal crops, exposing the ploughed soil to the strong winds and heavy rain of winter. The result on downland, and in other parts of Britain, including the Vale of York, has been increased soil erosion, mainly by surface runoff, but also by the wind as aeolian erosion.

Research carried out between 1982 and 1992 on the south facing dip slopes of the South Downs, identified annual rates of erosion between 0.5 and 5 cu m per hectare. They were particularly severe in the autumn and winter of 1982 and 1987 (Figure 5.2.2). The problem on the South Downs is not just confined to soil erosion. The combination of surface runoff and sediment has also caused the flooding of urban properties adjacent to the agricultural areas. The Brighton suburb of Bevendean was flooded in 1973, 1982, and 1987. Portslade near Hove was flooded in November 1976 and October 1987 but the worst event occurred on the 7 October 1987, when 30 houses in Rottingdean were flooded.

Apart from the change from spring to winter cereal crops, other causes of soil erosion on the South Downs have been related to:

- the intensification of farming, especially the replacement of organic farmyard manure by inorganic chemical fertilisers, which reduce the humus content and moisture holding capability of the soil,
- the ploughing of the steeper slopes,
- the creation of larger fields by the removal of hedgerows,
- the compaction of the soil by machinery decreasing infiltration and increasing surface runoff, and
- the production of a fine soil texture to aid seed germination, but which is more easily eroded by both water and wind.

The South Downs has been designated as an Environmentally Sensitive Area (ESA), and the Ministry of Agriculture, Fisheries and Food, in 1988, recommended the following practices to reduce soil erosion:

- return the land to permanent grass, especially on slopes over 11 degrees,
- increase the percentage of spring sown crops, leaving the stubble unploughed until February,
- produce a coarse soil texture (tilth),
- reduce compaction along vehicle wheel tracks,
- plough along the contour where possible, and
- restore hedges or leave grass strips across the slope gradient.

STUDENT ACTIVITY 5.8

1 Why is soil erosion such a problem on the South Downs?
2 How is the problem being managed?

Year	Rainfall total (mm) 1 Sept–1 Mar	Soil loss cu.m per hectare	Total soil loss cubic metres
82–83	724	1.7	1816
83–84	560	0.6	27
84–85	580	1.1	182
85–86	453	0.7	541
86–87	503	0.7	211
87–88	739	5.0	13 529
88–89	324	0.5	2
89–90	621	1.4	940
90–91	469	2.3	1527
91–92	298	1.2	112

FIGURE 5.2.2 Soil erosion on the South Downs, 1982–1992

5.3 Limestone Pavements

FIGURE 5.3.1 Limestone pavement, Yorkshire Dales

Limestone pavements are, in Britain, a rare and threatened type of calcareous habitat, with 43 per cent of their area being lost or damaged between 1945 and 1990. It has been estimated that they only cover a total area of 2 150 hectares, with only 813 hectares being unaffected by stone removal or movement. Eighty-eight per cent of the total limestone pavement area occurs in England. Limestone has been used as a rockery stone for building stonewalls, as a construction material, and as part of the Flue Gas Desulphurisation Process in the chimney stacks of coal burning power stations where it absorbs the sulphur dioxide, reducing the risk of acid rain.

Limestone pavement is produced when almost horizontal beds of limestone are weathered, mainly by chemical processes. Carbonic acid in rain water, and in the soil, reacts with the limestone which is mainly calcium carbonate ($CaCO_3$), dissolving it by a process called carbonation. The limestone has vertical lines of weakness, called joints, which are enlarged by the weathering process, forming deep fissures called grikes. The blocks between the grikes then form clints. Many of the clints have small channels (runnels), and depressions (cups), on their surface formed by weathering.

CASE STUDY

Scar Close, Ingleborough

Although the Yorkshire Dales National Park (YDNP), contains over half of Britain's limestone pavements, they cover only 1360 hectares (0.77 per cent) of the Park. Most of them are in the south west, where Carboniferous Great Scar Limestone outcrops, forming typical limestone or karst landscape, similar to that in the Burren National Park in Eire. Scar Close is part of the Ingleborough National Nature Reserve, and is a Site of Special Scientific Interest. Scar Close is a most impressive example of limestone pavement, with large clints and deep grikes. Very little vegetation is able to grow on the clints because of the harsh environment, but blue-grey algae is able to grow in some of the 'cups' on the clints, as is Yorkshire stonewort. Most plant life, however, is found in the grikes, which, although in shade, are less exposed to the wind and which have slightly more moist soil conditions. Wall rue, rigid buckler fern, and limestone polypody fern grow on the more exposed sites either in small grikes or the upper zones of the deeper grikes. As the depth increases, maidenhair spleenwort, and then brittle bladder-fern and green spleenwort occur. Conditions at the bottom of the grikes are similar to shady woodlands, and consequently, woodland species are found such as

dog's mercury, ramsons, herb Robert, and wood sorrel. Rare species such as baneberry, giant bellflower, and enchanter's nightshade are found in some grikes.

Over the limestone at lower altitudes a calcareous grassland community, with blue moor grass is dominant, and herbs including wild thyme, limestone bedstraw, common rock-rose and bloody crane's-bill have developed on the thin rendzina soils. In some areas, scrub, composed of hawthorn, ash, hazel, blackthorn, rowan, and bird cherry is able to grow.

Apart from the protection afforded by SSSI status, limestone pavements can now, under section 34 of the Wildlife and Countryside Act 1981, be protected by Limestone Pavement Orders, which make the removal of limestone rock a criminal offence.

5.4 Heathlands

Initially, it is believed that most heathlands were mainly restricted to altitudes above 300 m, and to areas with sandy soils. Today, as a result of extensive deforestation since the Neolithic period, heathlands have a much wider distribution. They occur on acidic soils, which have a low nutrient base. Heathlands can be classified either by drainage conditions, into dry heath or wet heath, or by altitude, into upland heath or lowland heath.

In many areas the heath community has a distinctive vertical structure (Figure 5.4.1). Dry heath has a canopy, composed mainly of ericaceous dwarf shrubs, especially ling or common heather (*Calluna vulgaris*), and bell heather (*Erica cinerea*) formed at approximately 40 cms. Beneath it is a herb layer with bilberry (*Vaccinium myrtillus*), crowberry (*Emperetrum nigrum*), dwarf gorse (*Ulex minor*), western gorse (*Ulex gallii*), and grasses including wavy hair grass (*Deschampsia flexuosa*).

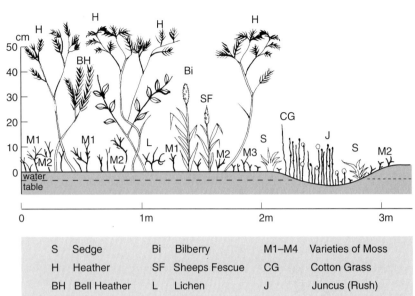

S	Sedge	Bi	Bilberry	M1–M4	Varieties of Moss
H	Heather	SF	Sheeps Fescue	CG	Cotton Grass
BH	Bell Heather	L	Lichen	J	Juncus (Rush)

FIGURE 5.4.1 Vertical structure of the heath community

FIGURE 5.4.2 The stages in the development of heather

FIGURE 5.4.6 Heath habitats

STUDENT ACTIVITY 5.9

1 Describe and explain the differences in the plant communities illustrated in Figure 5.4.1.
2 How would you expect the plant communities to change following:
a) burning, and
b) drainage?

The ground surface is a mixture of mosses and lichens. Wet heath tends to be more open, with a wider range of species, which as conditions become wetter become increasingly dominated by bog or mire species. It is usually dominated by cross leaved heather (*Erica tetralix*), mosses especially *Sphagnum spp.*, hare's tail cotton grass (*Eriophorum vaginatum*), heath rush (*Juncus squarrosus*), purple moor grass (*Molina caerulea*), and deer grass (*Scirpus cespitosus*).

Heather has a very distinctive life cycle, which is commonly divided into four main phases (Figures 5.4.2 and 5.4.3). After the degenerate phase, if new heather plants are unable to become established it is possible that the succession will continue with bracken initially becoming dominant, and then, under favourable conditions, being succeeded by birch, and possibly oak trees. In areas where the heather is managed for sheep grazing or grouse, it is burnt on an 8 to 15 year cycle to encourage new growth, and to control the progression of the natural succession.

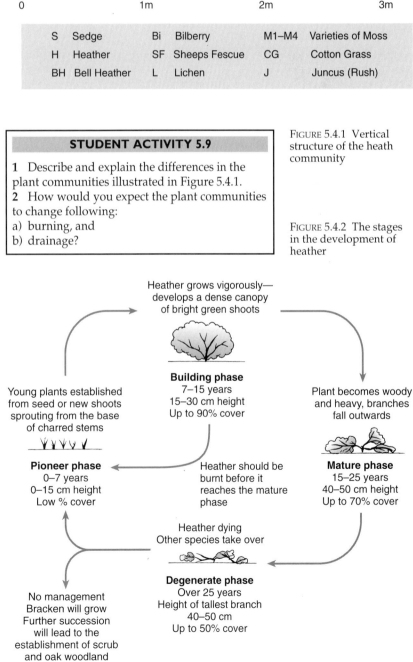

Heather grows vigorously— develops a dense canopy of bright green shoots

Building phase
7–15 years
15–30 cm height
Up to 90% cover

Plant becomes woody and heavy, branches fall outwards

Mature phase
15–25 years
40–50 cm height
Up to 70% cover

Young plants established from seed or new shoots sprouting from the base of charred stems

Pioneer phase
0–7 years
0–15 cm height
Low % cover

Heather should be burnt before it reaches the mature phase

Heather dying
Other species take over

Degenerate phase
Over 25 years
Height of tallest branch
40–50 cm
Up to 50% cover

No management
Bracken will grow
Further succession will lead to the establishment of scrub and oak woodland

FIGURE 5.4.3 The growth phases of heather

Growth phase	Pioneer	Building	Mature	Degenerate
Average age (yrs)	5.7	9.0	17.1	24.0
Biomass:				
Heather	287.2	1507.6	1923.6	1043.2
Other shrubs, grasses	179.6	41.2	52.0	83.2
Mosses	422.4	153.2	329.6	434.4
Total biomass g/sq.m	889.2	1702.0	2305.2	1560.8
Mean height cms	24.1	52.1	63.2	55.2
Light reaching surface (%)	100.0	2.0	20.0	57.0

FIGURE 5.4.4 The heathland nutrient cycle

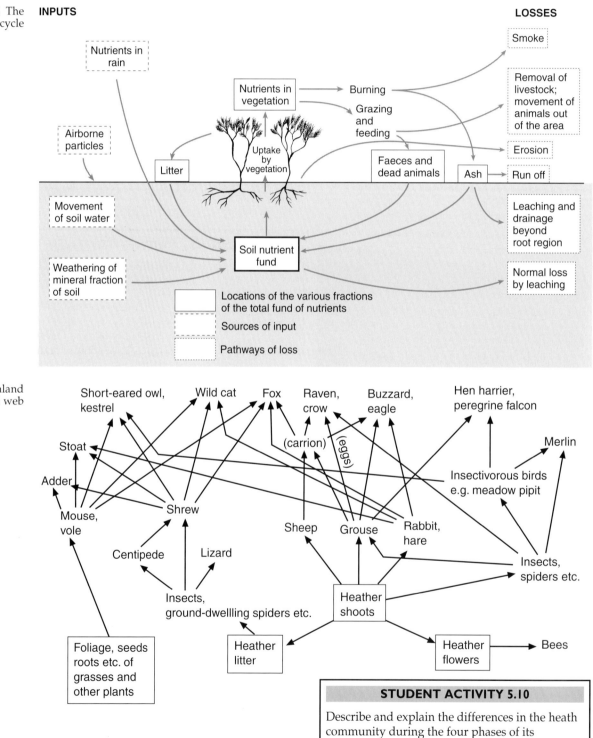

FIGURE 5.4.5 A heathland food web

STUDENT ACTIVITY 5.10

Describe and explain the differences in the heath community during the four phases of its development.

CASE STUDY

Lowland heath

Heathlands are generally classified as lowland heath if they occur below 250 m. Since 1800, 84 per cent of England's lowland heath has been lost, mainly to urbanisation and agricultural improvement. English Nature have estimated that there was 190 000 hectares of lowland heath in 1800, which had declined to 73 000 by 1940 and only 32 000 hectares by 1993.

County	Area hectares	County	Area hectares
Hampshire	9021	Norfolk	537
Cornwall	6416	East Sussex	388
Dorset	5365	Somerset	382
Surrey	2988	West Midlands	298
Devon	2362	Berkshire	293
Suffolk	942	North Yorkshire	293
Staffordshire	880	Shropshire	228
Cumbria	787	West Sussex	205

FIGURE 5.4.6 Counties with more than 200 hectares of lowland heath

FIGURE 5.4.7 Changes in the area of lowland heath, and National Nature Reserves in Dorset

Lowland heathland in Dorset

The data in Figure 5.4.8 clearly illustrates the alarming rate of loss of lowland heathland in Dorset. What the figures fail to show is the increasing fragmentation of the heathlands. In 1759, the Dorset heathlands consisted of approximately 10 large areas. In 1978, there were 768 smaller areas scattered across the county. Today, 94 per cent (5034 ha) of Dorset's lowland heath is protected by SSSI status, with six areas having National Nature Reserve status (Figure 5.4.7 and 5.4.8).

Large areas of heath are used for military training, and although access to them is restricted, this type of use has protected them from being lost to agriculture or urban growth.

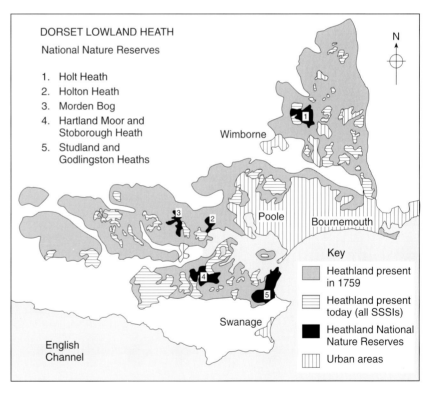

DORSET LOWLAND HEATH

National Nature Reserves

1. Holt Heath
2. Holton Heath
3. Morden Bog
4. Hartland Moor and Stoborough Heath
5. Studland and Godlingston Heaths

Key
- Heathland present in 1759
- Heathland present today (all SSSIs)
- Heathland National Nature Reserves
- Urban areas

FIGURE 5.4.8 Areas of lowland heath in Dorset

Date	Area '000 hectares	NNR	Area hectares
1750	39.6	Hartland Moor	243.2
1811	30.4	Holt Heath	488.2
1896	22.67	Holton Heath	117.0
1934	18.22	Morden Bog	148.5
1960	10.0	Stoborough Heath	108.9
1978	5.83	Studland Heath	630.8
1992	5.6		

FIGURE 5.4.9 Upland heath in the National Parks

	Brecon Beacons	Broads	Dartmoor	Exmoor	Lake District	Northumberland	North York Moors	Peak District	Pembrokeshire	Snowdonia	Yorkshire Dales
Upland heath sq. km	121.6	0.0	207.8	92.4	123.5	201.1	355.7	222	37.2	304.2	266.3
Percentage of total	9.0	0.0	21.8	13.3	5.4	19.2	24.8	15.4	6.4	14.2	15.1
Change 1970–80 sq. km	−6.6	0.0	−0.5	−5.3	+1.7	−16.4	+3.2	−2.7	−2.6	−15.9	+3.4

Hartland Moor and Stoborough National Nature Reserves

These two reserves are adjacent to each other (Figure 5.4.7), and are located to the south west of Poole Harbour. They cover 353 hectares, and form part of the 650 hectare Hartland Moor Initiative. The reserves are owned and managed by English Nature, and the National Trust, and have a mixture of dry and wet heath, together with valley mire or bog.

FIGURE 5.4.10 Natural areas in England containing upland or lowland heath

In the hot dry summer of 1976, over 90 per cent of Hartland Moor was burnt by one fire. Now, the area is covered by a network of firebreaks, linked to deep Emergency Water Supply pools. Since 1976, the heather has regrown, but in some areas pine, birch and gorse are invasive, and have to be managed by a programme of controlled burning, normally carried out during the winter months. This also maintains a mosaic of communities of different ages, heights and species. The Reserves are part of the Hartland Moor Initiative which aims to improve the quality of the existing heathlands, and to restore agricultural land back to heath. The Initiative uses funds from English Nature's Wildlife Enhancement Scheme, and the Countryside Commission's Countryside Stewardship Scheme. Over the past 40 years the Reserves have not been grazed and this has allowed the invasion of scrub species. To combat this a traditional grazing programme, involving Exmoor ponies and Red Devon cattle, is being introduced. To the south of the Reserves agricultural land previously part of New Lines and Hartland Farms is being restored to heath and acid grassland. It is hoped that the Reserves will act as a reservoir of species, which will then expand to colonise the reclaimed areas. The agricultural land is being reclaimed by ploughing which brings dormant heather seeds, which can survive for over 40 years in the soil, to the surface. Soil fertility is then decreased, and acidity increased by adding sulphur, and new heather and other wild plant seeds are scattered over the reclaimed areas.

In 1993, English Nature launched the Lowland Heathland Programme, which aimed at highlighting the importance of lowland heathland for species including the sand lizard, the Dartford warbler, smooth snake, the marsh gentian and silver studded blue butterfly, and also provided funding for the restoration of neglected heathlands.

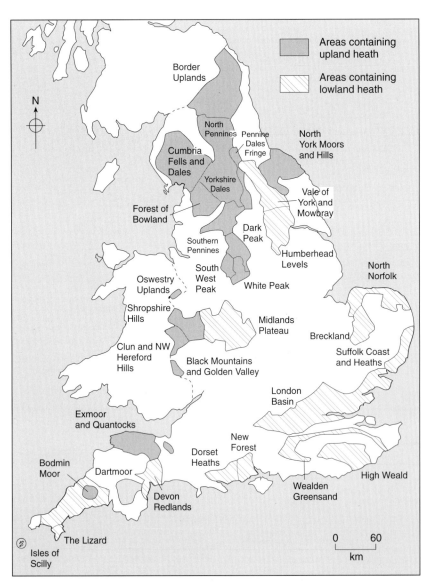

Areas containing upland heath

Areas containing lowland heath

N

Border Uplands
North Pennines
Pennine Dales Fringe
North York Moors and Hills
Cumbria Fells and Dales
Yorkshire Dales
Forest of Bowland
Vale of York and Mowbray
Dark Peak
Southern Pennines
Humberhead Levels
South West Peak
North Norfolk
Oswestry Uplands
White Peak
Shropshire Hills
Midlands Plateau
Breckland
Clun and NW Hereford Hills
Black Mountains and Golden Valley
Suffolk Coast and Heaths
London Basin
Exmoor and Quantocks
New Forest
Dorset Heaths
High Weald
Bodmin Moor
Dartmoor
Wealden Greensand
Devon Redlands
The Lizard
Isles of Scilly

0   60
km

STUDENT ACTIVITY 5.13

Refer to Figures 5.4.9 and 5.4.10 and:
1 Analyse the distribution of lowland and upland heath shown on Figure 5.4.10.
2 Describe the differences between the parks in the areas of upland heath.
3 Suggest reasons to explain the changes between 1970–80.

5.5 Freshwater Wetlands

■ Freshwater wetlands include a variety of habitats ranging from productive base rich fens with a diverse range of species, to acidic nutrient and species poor peatlands. As with many other habitats, freshwater wetlands are facing threats from several types of human activities.

■ In 1996 the Biodiversity Challenge Group, consisting of the Royal Society for the Protection of Birds, Friends of the Earth, the World Wide Fund for Nature, Plantlife, the Wildlife Trusts, and Butterfly Conservation reported that at least 354 'protected' wetland wildlife sites in Britain were being affected by the mismanagement of water. In 1998, both the Environment Agency, and English Nature published similar reports.

Rivers and lakes

Rivers and lakes can be classified by their nutrient status (Figure 5.5.1), which determines their plant and animal life. The water quality of many lakes and rivers has been badly affected by phosphate rich discharges from domestic sewage, and nitrates from agricultural runoff resulting in **eutrophication**. Heavy metals and organic chemicals in industrial waste have added to the problem of pollution.

As well as the problem of eutrophication, referred to above, lakes are being affected by:

■ acidification, from both acid rain and acidic runoff from coniferous plantations,
■ the introduction of non-native species such as Canadian pondweed,
■ their use for public drinking water,
■ the production of hydro-electric power, and
■ recreational pressures, such as powerboating on Lake Windermere.

Many lakes exhibit a zonal sequence of vegetation types called a **hydrosere**, linked to water depth (Figure 5.5.2).

Riparian areas, river channels and their floodplains provide many types of habitat including fast flowing turbulent water, gravel beds, sand banks, marshes and wet grassland.

Type	Nutrient status	Characteristics
Eutrophic	Nutrient rich	Water often strongly discoloured by algae, pH usually over 7. Bed often highly organic mud
Mesotrophic	Intermediate level of nutrients	Water sometimes discoloured by planktonic algae, pH usually around or slightly below neutral
Oligotrophic	Poor in plant nutrients	Water very clear, plankton sparse. pH usually less than 7. Bed rocky, sandy or peaty
Dystrophic	Very poor in plant nutrients, particularly available nitrogen	Water usually peat stained. pH very low (3.5–5.5). Alkalinity very low (below 2 mg/l CaCO$_3$)
Marl	Rich in calcium	Water very clear. Alkalinity at least 100 mg/l CaCO$_3$. Powdery deposit of marl covers lake bed.

FIGURE 5.5.1 A classification of rivers and lakes by nutrient status

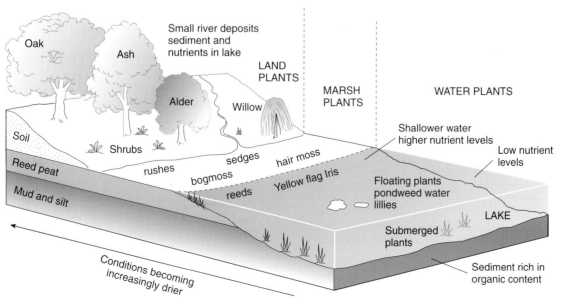

FIGURE 5.5.2 A typical lake hydrosere

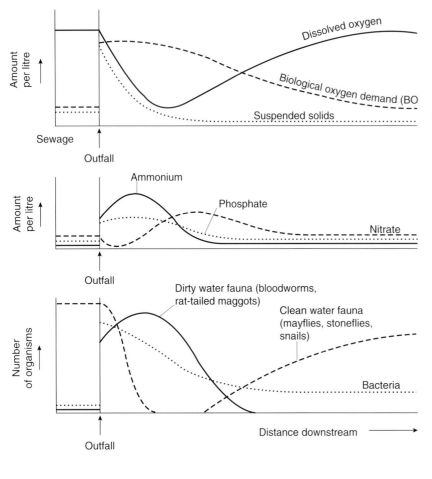

FIGURE 5.5.3 The effects on water quality of organic effluent at, and downstream of, a sewage treatment works

1 *Channelisation and flood control* – Many rivers, especially in the lowlands have been straightened, widened and deepened to reduce the flood risk to urban areas and agricultural land. The increased velocity and discharge produced by these alterations seriously affects the nature of the river's plants and animals.

2 *Loss of washlands* – Many floodplains or washlands have been drained and built on, and the flooding of the washlands has been prevented by the building of high levees.

3 *Water abstraction* – The water in many rivers is removed, or **abstracted**, for domestic, industrial and agricultural use. This is particularly a problem in summer when low flow conditions may result in an increase in pollution levels.

4 *Inter basin water transfer* – Many water companies transfer river water from one river basin to another. Water is now able to be transferred from the River Tyne to the River Ouse in Yorkshire.

5 *Alien species* – Many rivers have been affected by the introduction of non-native species. These have included American mink, American signal crayfish, Japanese knotweed, giant hogweed, and the Himalayan basalm.

The monitoring of river water quality

The Environment Agency (EA) monitors, monthly, the water quality at 8000 sites on 40 000 kilometres of the rivers of England and Wales. The system used is called the General Quality Assessment (GQA), and at the present time it includes the Chemical GQA and the Biological GQA. The Chemical GQA describes the quality of rivers in terms of the measurements, which detect the most common types of pollution, that is, discharges of organic wastes from sewage treatment works, agriculture and industry (Figure 5.5.4). The Biological GQA monitors the small animal population, particularly macro invertebrates, on the river bed. Animals such as stoneflies and mayflies are the least tolerant of polluted conditions, unlike midge larvae and worms, which can tolerate low oxygen conditions. The Nutrient GQA is being developed to measure the level of phosphate in rivers, and the Aesthetic GQA will measure the 'appearance' of a river.

STUDENT ACTIVITY 5.14

Describe and explain the effect of a sewage treatment works on water quality, as illustrated by Figure 5.5.3.

The main natural processes of rivers are to transport water and eroded material (sediment), and to provide a habitat for wildlife. English rivers contain one-third (600 species) of the country's plant life. The increasing use of rivers for human activities is, in many cases, substantially modifying these natural processes, through pollution, and:

FIGURE 5.5.4 Chemical GQA water classification

Water quality	Grade	Dissolved oxygen	Biochemical oxygen demand (BOD)	Ammonia
		% saturation	mg/l	mg/l
Very good	A	80	2.5	0.25
Good	B	70	4	0.6
Fairly good	C	60	6	1.3
Fair	D	50	8	2.5
Poor	E	20	15	9
Bad	F	less than 20	over 15	over 9

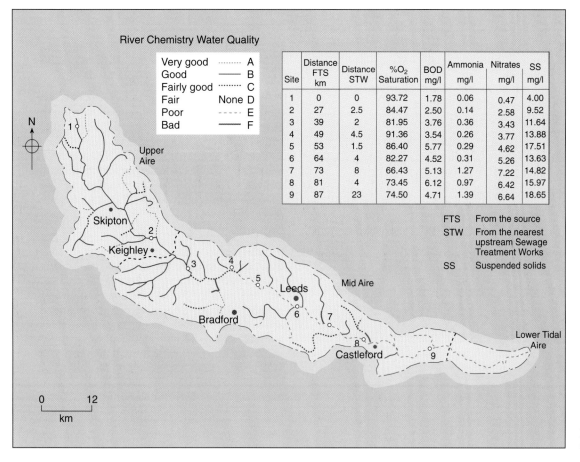

River Chemistry Water Quality

	Very good	....	A
	Good	——	B
	Fairly good	....	C
	Fair	None	D
	Poor	- - - -	E
	Bad	——	F

Site	Distance FTS km	Distance STW	%O₂ Saturation	BOD mg/l	Ammonia mg/l	Nitrates mg/l	SS mg/l
1	0	0	93.72	1.78	0.06	0.47	4.00
2	27	2.5	84.47	2.50	0.14	2.58	9.52
3	39	2	81.95	3.76	0.36	3.43	11.64
4	49	4.5	91.36	3.54	0.26	3.77	13.88
5	53	1.5	86.40	5.77	0.29	4.62	17.51
6	64	4	82.27	4.52	0.31	5.26	13.63
7	73	8	66.43	5.13	1.27	7.22	14.82
8	81	4	73.45	6.12	0.97	6.42	15.97
9	87	23	74.50	4.71	1.39	6.64	18.65

FTS   From the source
STW   From the nearest upstream Sewage Treatment Works
SS   Suspended solids

FIGURE 5.5.5 The water quality of the River Aire

STUDENT ACTIVITY 5.15

1 How does the water quality of the River Aire vary throughout its catchment area (Figure 5.5.5)?

2 An analysis of the data has shown that:

■ the correlation between distance from the source (DFS) and dissolved oxygen is −0.69 (significant at the 99% level), and

■ the correlation between DFS and nitrate levels is +0.97 (significant at the 99.9% level). Interpret these correlations.

Mires or peatlands

The mires or peatlands of Britain cover 6 per cent (1 645 970 hectares) of the surface, and represent the ninth largest area of peat in the world. Mires or peatlands are wetlands that support a peat forming type of vegetation, commonly including various species of bog moss *Sphagnum spp.*, and where the peat is over 0.5 m thick. The peat accumulates as the low oxygen (*anaerobic*) waterlogged conditions associated with the high water table slow down the rate of decomposition of plant material. Rates of peat accumulation are very low averaging approximately 0.5 mm per year. Vertically, peatlands consist of two layers. At the surface is the active zone or *acrotelm*, which contains the living plants. Beneath it is the zone of peat accumulation called the *catotelm*, which may be up to 10 m deep.

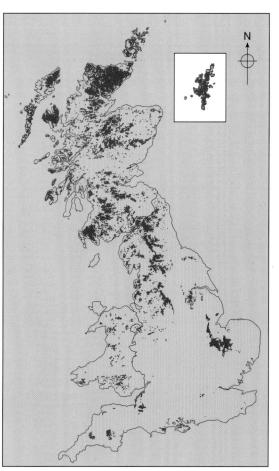

FIGURE 5.5.6 Areas of deep peat soils in Britain

Raised bog

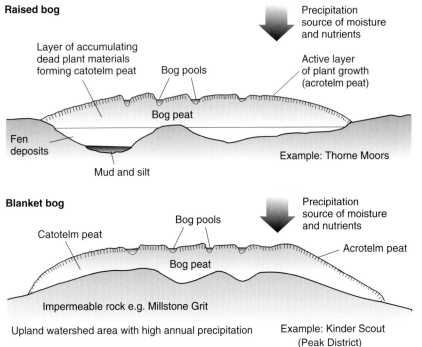

Precipitation source of moisture and nutrients

Layer of accumulating dead plant materials forming catotelm peat

Bog pools

Active layer of plant growth (acrotelm peat)

Bog peat

Fen deposits

Mud and silt

Example: Thorne Moors

Blanket bog

Catotelm peat

Bog pools

Precipitation source of moisture and nutrients

Acrotelm peat

Bog peat

Impermeable rock e.g. Millstone Grit

Upland watershed area with high annual precipitation

Example: Kinder Scout (Peak District)

FIGURE 5.5.7 Raised and blanket bogs

Mires are usually classified into different types, based on their water and nutrient source.

1 Fens are **minerotrophic** mires, which receive most of their water and nutrients from groundwater or springs. They can be further subdivided into valley, basin and floodplain fens.

2 Bogs are **ombrotrophic** mires. These types of mires receive water and nutrients from rainwater (*ombros* = rain storm, *trophos* = feeder), and are characterised by a low nutrient status (*oligotrophic*) and a high level of acidity. The two main types of bogs are:

■ Raised bogs – These normally occur in waterlogged lowland areas, and begin as fen lakes. Gradually over time as the fen vegetation dies and becomes peat, the fen lake becomes shallower until a stage is reached where the central peat area is above the original water table level. From this point a raised bog has been formed, which now receives water and nutrients from rainfall (Figure 5.5.7).

FIGURE 5.5.8 Peat areas in Britain (hectares)

Country	Fen	Raised bog	Blanket bog	Intermediate bog	Total area
England	131 672	37 413	214 138	981	384 204
Scotland	1215	27 892	1 056 198	10 653	1 095 958
Wales	2867	4086	158 770	85	165 808
Total	135 754	69 391	1 429 106	11 719	1 645 970

FIGURE 5.5.9 The peatland mire ecosystem

STUDENT ACTIVITY 5.16

Suggest reasons to explain the distribution of peat areas shown by Figures 5.5.6 and 5.5.8.

■ Blanket bogs – On undulating impermeable rock surfaces in the uplands, where rainfall is high, bog communities initially form in the pools in the depressions. Gradually, they expand and spread out and across the rock surface, forming the type of extensive blanket bog systems seen on the plateau summit areas of the Pennines and Dartmoor (Figure 5.5.7).

Mires, particularly in the uplands, are important controllers of river levels, providing a source of water during dry periods, and storing water at wetter times. Bog mosses *Sphagnum spp.* act as sponges absorbing up to twenty times their own weight in water. Many blanket bogs in areas such as the Pennines, have been drained to permit increased stocking levels of sheep. As they dry out they are very susceptible to erosion from runoff and by the wind. In other areas they are being drained for afforestation. In lowland areas, many peatlands, for example the Fens have been converted to agriculture, or have been worked commercially for peat compost.

The process of peat formation locks up atmospheric carbon as fossil carbon. The drainage of peatlands releases this carbon back into the atmosphere at the rate of 1000 tonnes of carbon per hectare, for each metre depth, adding to the effects of global warming from other sources of carbon dioxide.

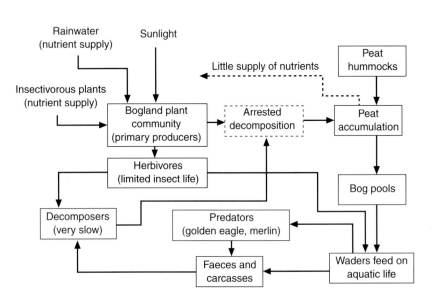

Rainwater (nutrient supply)

Sunlight

Little supply of nutrients

Peat hummocks

Insectivorous plants (nutrient supply)

Bogland plant community (primary producers)

Arrested decomposition

Peat accumulation

Herbivores (limited insect life)

Bog pools

Decomposers (very slow)

Predators (golden eagle, merlin)

Faeces and carcasses

Waders feed on aquatic life

CASE STUDY

The Humberhead Levels

Thorne, Hatfield, Goole, and Crowle Moors form the largest complex of lowland raised bog in Britain, and are the remnants of an extensive lowland raised bog which has covered the Humberhead Levels since the Atlantic Period over 7000 years ago. In recent years, considerable concern has been expressed over their management, and the role of English Nature.

Thorne and Hatfield Moors, at 1900 hectares and 1400 hectares, respectively, are the largest lowland raised bogs in Britain, and have been worked for peat for many centuries. Initially, the peat was used for fuel and animal litter for livestock. More recently, peat has been extracted commercially for use in horticulture and gardens.

A brief history of the Thorne and Hatfield Moors controversy

Planning permission for peat extraction from Thorne and Hatfield Moors was first granted in 1951. In 1963, Fisons (now Levington Horticultural) acquired Thorne and Hatfield Moors for commercial use. Concern over the rate of peat loss resulted, in 1970, in the two moors being declared SSSIs by the Nature Conservancy Council. In 1985, parts of Thorne and Crowle Moors were designated the Humberhead Peatlands National Nature Reserve. Peat extraction continued, and, in 1987, Fisons adopted a new more destructive form of extraction known as 'milling', which exposed large areas of bare peat. In 1991, B&Q the largest of the d-i-y companies, announced that it would no longer buy peat extracted from SSSIs. Fisons, in January 1992, then announced that it was donating nearly all of its peatlands, including Thorne and Hatfield Moors, to English Nature. Some of the sites were in good condition for wildlife, others had been drained and stripped and needed restoration work. Fisons still held planning consents to remove peat from all of the sites. In 1994, all 3250 hectares of Fisons' lowland peatlands were handed over to English Nature. English Nature then announced it was leasing 2000 hectares back to Fisons, and their business successor Levington Horticulture, on condition that they were worked to an agreed depth, leaving an average of half a metre of peat which would permit future restoration for wildlife. The remaining areas with suitable habitats were to be conserved as nature reserves, and the worked out areas were to be restored. In 1997, English Nature proposed, on the grounds that these areas no longer met the required standards, to denotify from the designated SSSI areas, 100 hectares of Thorne Moors, and 490 hectares of Hatfield Moors. The areas consisted of bare deep peat, which could be worked by Levington to produce peat from a non SSSI source. Opposition to the proposal quickly came from the Yorkshire Wildlife Trust, the Thorne

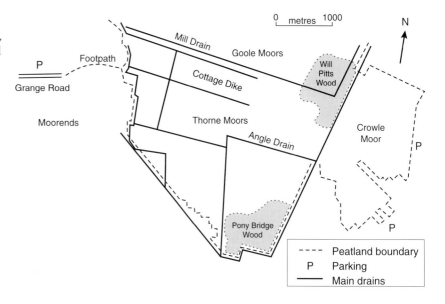

FIGURE 5.5.10
Humberhead Peatlands NNR

and Hatfield Moors Conservation Forum, the Peatlands Campaign Consortium, and the Environment Agency. On December 2 1997, English Nature announced that it no longer intended to continue with the proposal.

The Humberhead Peatlands National Nature Reserve was created in 1985, and consists of the abandoned peat workings of Thorne and Crowle Moors. The Reserve is managed by English Nature, and the Lincolnshire Trust for Nature Conservation. It is an important wildlife site with over 700 plant, 3000 invertebrate, and almost 200 bird species, including twenty-five rare species, examples being the large heath butterfly, the insectivorous bladderwort, and the European nightjar.

The primary management aim of the Reserve is to maintain the raised bog habitat and its associated wildlife. In order to maintain or increase the water table, a programme of *rewetting* is being undertaken. So far, 2500 dams have been constructed along the old drainage channels, and 35 m gallons of water have been pumped from the main cuts where peat is being extracted into the old cuttings. Low banks have also been built to collect surface runoff. These attempts to improve the water levels have faced two problems. Firstly, a bog is a hydrological unit, and the drainage ditches cut in order to extract the peat in one area affect other areas. Between 1980 and 1990 an additional 24 km of drains were cut on Thorne Moors. In February 1990, drainage works in the south east of Thorne Moors lowered the water table by 60 cm. Secondly, as in other parts of the country, there appears to be an increasing number of years when the annual rainfall is below the average. The summers of both 1989 and 1990 were drier than usual, and in 1996 annual rainfall was 478.7 mm compared with the long term average of 605 mm. The drier conditions have helped the expansion over the Moors of unwanted birch scrub and rhododendrons. A programme to control rhododendrons on Thorne Moors is now being undertaken, and birch scrub on Crowle Moors is being cleared and then controlled by the grazing of Hebridean sheep.

STUDENT ACTIVITY 5.17

1 Outline the views held in the Thorne and Hatfield Moors controversy by
(i) Fisons/Levington Horticultural (ii) English Nature and (iii) conservation groups such as the Yorkshire Wildlife Trust.
2 Which point of view do you support? Why?

Use of peat

Approximately 3 m cu m of peat are used annually in the UK. Most of it is used by horticulture and for garden peat and compost. It has been estimated that at present rates of extraction, horticultural peat reserves will have been exhausted within 20 years. Conservationists believe that there are several alternatives to peat, whose use would then help to protect the remaining peatlands. They include composted bark and wood waste from the timber industry, coir fibre (a waste product from the coconut industry), and composted garden waste.

CASE STUDY

The Fir Wars – the battle for the Flow Country

Although Scotland contains approximately 10 500 sq km of blanket bog (14 per cent of its surface) concern over the increasing rate of its loss, especially to coniferous plantations, led in the 1980s to a national debate which became known as the 'Fir Wars'. The Flow Country in Caithness and Sutherland, covering almost 4 000 sq km, is probably the largest single expanse of blanket bog in the world (Figure 5.5.11). It is a unique bog/wet heath system, including tundra plants normally only found further north, which provides a habitat for a very wide range of breeding birds, especially greenshank, dunlin, and golden plover.

FIGURE 5.5.11 Flow Country

Afforestation in the Flow Country began seriously after 1981, as new machinery, including the boat or peat plough allowed planting on deep peat. By 1985, 67 000 hectares had been converted to forest, mainly of lodgepole pine. The Forestry Commission were responsible for planting 21 500 hectares, with private companies especially Fountain Forestry who planted 40 000 hectares, being responsible for the remainder. Many private individuals were involved as planting provided a financial gain through tax benefits. In 1985, the Royal Society for the Protection of Birds (RSPB) expressed their concern over the loss of habitat, and the consequent decline in the bird populations. In 1986–87, Fountain Forestry announced plans for the planting of a further 39 000 hectares, on the grounds that this would provide the 100 000 hectares required to make the local timber processing industry viable. On the 23 July 1987, there were two press conferences about forestry in the Flow Country. In London, the Nature Conservancy Council (NCC) and RSPB in '*Birds, Bogs and Forestry: the Peatlands of Caithness and Sutherland*' stated their opposition to any further loss of peatland habitats. Meanwhile, in Inverness, the Highlands and Islands Development Board (HIDB) stressed the need for the expansion of forestry to retain the 2000 jobs provided by the industry. In order to resolve the issue a working party was set up by the Highland Regional Council, consisting of representatives from the HIDB, NCC, and the Countryside Commission for Scotland. It reported in 1989, and recommended that an extra 39 000 hectares of planting should be permitted over the following 20 years. Based on nature conservation, deer management, landscape, recreation, archaeology, and agriculture the report also divided the Flow Country into four categories: areas where planting would be 'preferable', 'possible', 'undesirable' or 'unsuitable'.

CASE STUDY

The Broads

The Broads contain a variety of freshwater habitats including the broads (lakes), rivers, fens, and freshwater grazing marshes. The major present habitats are shown in Figure 5.5.12. During the past 50 years, all of these habitats have been increasingly affected by human activities.

The broads (lakes)

The broads are the remnants of medieval peat diggings, which were then flooded, as a result of land subsidence, and a rise in sea level. The major threats they are facing include:

1 *Eutrophication* – The water quality of the broads has been particularly affected by the discharge into them of nutrients, especially phosphates (mainly from domestic sewage), and nitrates (mainly from agricultural runoff), resulting in changes to their nutrient state. Four phases of change have been recognised:

- *pre 1880*: low nutrient status (*oligotrophic*), phosphate levels of 20 mg/l with clear water, low growing plants on the lake beds and reedbeds on the lake edges,
- *1880s–1940s*: increasing nutrient status (*mesotrophic*), low growing plants replaced by taller water plants providing a suitable habitat for a range of invertebrates which provided food for both fish and wildfowl,
- *1950s–1980s*: high nutrient status (*eutrophic*) with phosphate levels of 100 mg/l, many submerged water plants and reedswamps had disappeared, from all but seven of the broads, to be replaced by vast numbers of phytoplankton (microscopic algae) turning the water cloudy and reducing light penetration,
- *1980s–1990s*: eutrophic conditions with phosphate levels of 1000 mg/l, six broads are dominated by blue-green algae, with toxic algal blooms in hot sunny weather, aquatic plants die reducing the number of water fleas which in turn cause the fish to die.

Solutions to the problem

Two methods are being used to manage the problem. The addition of ferric sulphate to domestic sewage, at the sewage treatment works, has the effect of removing 90 per cent of the phosphate, through a process known as **phosphate stripping**. At Ormesby Broad a procedure called *biomanipulation* is being used. Water fleas eat algae, and clear the water, but, in turn, they are eaten by fish. Biomanipulation involves temporarily removing the fish, 300 150 in 1995 at Ormesby, allowing the water fleas to multiply and clear the algae. To prevent the returned fish from eating them the young emerging water plants are, initially, protected by cages.

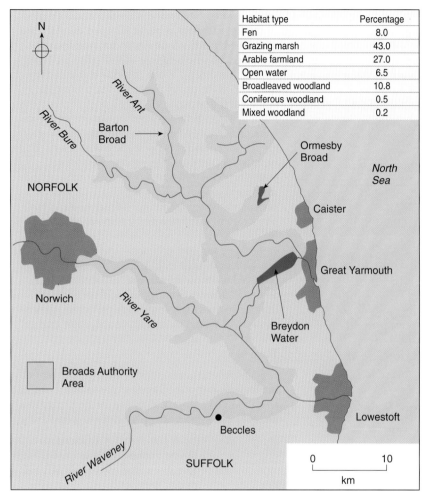

Habitat type	Percentage
Fen	8.0
Grazing marsh	43.0
Arable farmland	27.0
Open water	6.5
Broadleaved woodland	10.8
Coniferous woodland	0.5
Mixed woodland	0.2

Algae → water flea → perch → pike
Freshwater food chain

FIGURE 5.5.12 The Broads Authority Area and its habitats

2 *Bank erosion* – Many of the broads are suffering from severe bank erosion. Several factors are contributing to the problem including the decline of bank edge reed swamps due to eutrophication, wash and propeller turbulence from boats, and the effects of dredging. The eroded sediment is eventually deposited on the beds of the broads, and rates of sedimentation have increased from 1mm per year before 1950 to 12.8 mm per year in the 1970s causing many broads to become shallower. An additional problem is that the sediment contains nutrients, especially phosphates, which are released when the sediment is disturbed.

Solutions to the problem

The banks of the broads can be protected by creating natural protection through encouraging the growth of reed swamps or trees such as alder, willow, and sallow. Artificial protection may involve a wide range of materials from geotextile matting, through steel piling to concrete walls.

The sediment can be controlled by dredging, or suction pumping. Suction or mud pumping is part of a 5 year plan, between 1995 and 2000, at Barton Broad to remove phosphate rich sediment. The plan involves removing between 250 000 and 330 000 cu m of mud, which is being pumped into lagoons on adjacent fields where it will dry, and then be ploughed into the fields. Another technique being used is iron dosing. Ferric chloride is injected into the mud on the bed of the broads to control the release of the phosphate.

3 *Agricultural pollution from farm waste* – Pollution from farm waste comes from two main sources. Firstly, silage liquor may escape from silos or silage clamps. It is very toxic being 200 times more polluting than domestic sewage. Secondly, animal slurry and yard washings, which are high in phosphates, are washed into ditches and rivers. More careful management by farmers obviously reduces the risk of a pollution incident.

4 *Boatyard and craft pollution* – Diesel and engine oil is occasionally spilt from both boatyards and powered boats on the broads.

5 *Land drainage* – Some of the acid soils when drained release ferric hydroxide or 'ochre', which causes sedimentation and stains the water orange.

The fens

Fenland habitat covers 2500 hectares, 8 per cent of the Broads, and is the largest expanse of species rich fens in lowland Britain. Fens are the first stage in a natural succession from open water to woodland:

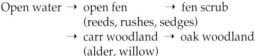

Open water → open fen   → fen scrub
              (reeds, rushes, sedges)
          → carr woodland → oak woodland
              (alder, willow)

FIGURE 5.5.13 The effect of human activities on the Broads

The fens need to be carefully managed to maintain the stage of the succession that is required. Open fen is the most species rich, and its management requires the water table to be maintained at the correct level, and the cutting of marsh hay, sedges, reeds, and tall herb fen at different times to create a mixture of plants at different stages of growth and height. In 1996, English Nature and the Broads Authority produced a *'Fen Management Strategy'* which outlines a programme for the consistent management of the fens.

The grazing marshes

Since the eighteenth century, the wet grassland marshes have been drained and 'improved', and today, drained marshes cover 43 per cent (20 000 hectares) of the Broads. During the 1970s and 1980s the rate of 'improvement' increased, with some marshes being drained and converted to arable farming. Britain joined the European Economic Community in 1973, and the Common Agricultural Policy (CAP) provided guaranteed prices for cereal crops which made arable farming more profitable than dairy farming, which was subjected to milk quotas. Between 1980 and 1983, 320 hectares annually were converted to arable farming, and by 1987, 30 per cent of the drained marshes had been converted to arable land. This intensification of farming, which involved the draining of the marshes and the application of fertilisers, pesticides and herbicides had profound effects upon the ecology of the marshes (Figure 5.5.13).

In 1984, the Halvergate Marshes, at 1 200 hectares the largest single area of grazing marsh in Britain, was at risk of being ploughed for arable farming. To prevent any changes, in 1985 the Ministry of Agriculture, Forestry and Fishing (MAFF), together with the Countryside Commission, established the *Broads Grazing Marshes Conservation Scheme*, through which farmers were paid £123 per hectare per year if they agreed:

■ not to plough up grazing marshes
■ to keep livestock on permanent grassland
■ to keep a low average stocking density of not more than 3 head of cattle, or 15 sheep per hectare
■ only to cut hay or silage once a year, and
■ to keep their use of nitrogen fertiliser at present levels.

In March 1987, the Broads was made an Environmentally Sensitive Area (ESA), and became eligible for a range of grants.

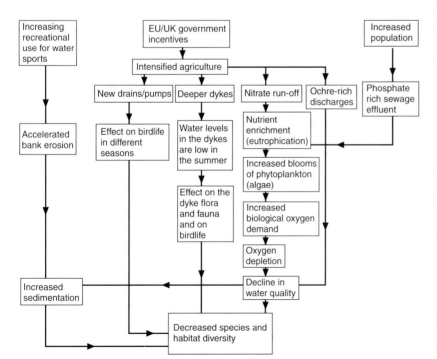

STUDENT ACTIVITY 5.18

1 Explain the term *eutrophication*.
2 Describe how the problem of eutrophication is being managed by the Broads Authority.
3 Tourism is an important source of income for the area, but it is causing a range of environmental problems. Identify the problems and explain how they may be managed.

5.6 Estuaries

In 'The Conservation of Estuaries', the Nature Conservancy Council defined an estuary as 'the mouth of a river through which freshwater is discharged to the sea, and where salt and freshwater mix to produce a zone of brackish water'. Britain has over 300 estuaries, formed as the sea level rose after the last ice age, and many estuaries are under considerable pressure from a variety of developments, including land reclamation for industry and housing, barrages, and pollution. In 1992, in response to the concern being expressed by such groups as the Royal Society for the Protection of Birds, and the Marine Conservation Society, the Government produced *Coastal Zone Protection and Planning*, and *Planning Policy and Guidance 20, Coastal Planning*, which stressed the need for an overall management strategy for estuaries. English Nature also announced the introduction of its *Estuaries Initiative* programme under which estuary management plans, such as the *Tees Estuary Management Plan* (see below), would be prepared linking economic development and wildlife conservation.

Estuaries are a highly productive ecosystem, with an average net primary productivity of 1500 g/sq.m/yr. Primary productivity is carried out by phytoplankton, and sea bed plants in the tidal channel, algae and plants on the intertidal mud and sandflats, and plants in the salt marshes and sand dunes. Estuaries are usually nutrient rich, with nutrient sources from river sediments, the sea, and released by current activity from the sediments on the bed of the estuary. The twice daily tidal cycle, however, also means that life has to be adapted to considerable variations in water salinity, inundation level, temperature, and turbidity. These variations combine to produce a wide variety of habitats, supporting numerous species, and interrelated by a complex food web (Figure 5.6.1).

These include lugworms, tubeworms, mud shrimps, cockles, Baltic tellin, Gaper shell, and mudsnails (up to 42 000 per cu m), all of which live in the mud. Wading birds, with bills and legs of different lengths, occupy specific niches. The shorter billed and shorter legged dunlin and knot feed on worms and small snails at the water's edge, with the longer legged and longer billed curlew and redshank, able to feed on lugworms and bivalve molluscs in deeper water. Wildfowl, including overwintering brent geese, barnacle geese, wigeon duck, teal duck, and mallard duck feed on the eelgrass, green seaweed and the saltmarsh grass. Offshore, eider ducks, goldeneye ducks and scoters dive for subtidal invertebrates.

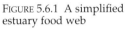

Figure 5.6.1 A simplified estuary food web

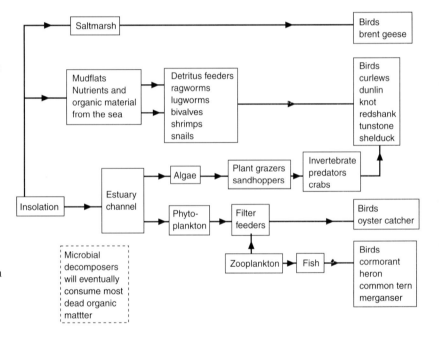

The tidal channel

The tidal channel is the habitat for a variety of:

- fish, including flounder, grey mullet, common goby, European eel, and the Atlantic salmon,
- crustaceans including crabs and lobsters,
- mammals including the otter, grey seal, common seal, and dolphins, and
- birds such as cormorants, mergansers, grebes, divers and herons.

The intertidal mud and sandflats

The intertidal mudflats are very productive, and a most important source of food for both resident and migrating bird populations. The mudflats may be covered by algae and eelgrass, and contain high population densities of detritus feeders.

Salt marshes

Five hundred years ago it has been estimated that there were 100 000 hectares of salt marsh in Britain. Today, the figure is approximately 45 000 hectares, of which 6750 hectares are in Wales, and 6000 hectares in Scotland. It is difficult to obtain exact figures because salt marshes are either being eroded naturally, or being lost to land reclamation, or accreting, that is expanding by the deposition of sediment and the colonisation by plants. Their stage of development can be related to the dominant plant community type.

Salt marshes can initially only be colonised by salt-tolerant plants, such as the seaweed *Enteromorpha*, eelgrass, and cord grass, which can withstand the twice daily inundation by the sea.

FIGURE 5.6.2 Salt marsh habitats

FIGURE 5.6.3 Salt marsh (halosere) succession

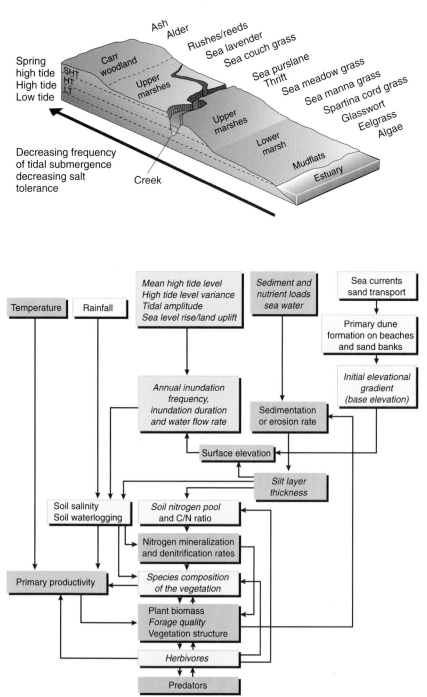

Once they are established, their roots are able to trap sediment, and nutrients, especially nitrogen, and gradually increase the height of the land producing a salt marsh. Rates of growth of salt marshes are usually between 0.001 cm and 10 cm a year. Figure 5.6.3 illustrates a typical example of a salt marsh (**halosere**) succession.

In many areas including the Solway Firth, Morecambe Bay, and Essex, salt marshes are used for grazing by both cattle and sheep. This often involves the enclosure of the upper marshes and their eventual 'improvement' by seeding, draining, and the use of fertilisers. In the Wash Estuary, 32 000 hectares have been reclaimed since the sixteenth century, and 20 000 hectares, mainly around the Crouch and Blackwater estuaries, have been reclaimed along the Essex coast.

The intertidal mudflats and salt marshes of Britain are believed to be the feeding and/or overwintering ground for over 2 m waders and 1 m wildfowl. Any loss of these habitats is therefore critical.

Sand dunes

The distribution of the major British sand dune complexes is shown on Figure 5.6.5. Sand dunes are depositional landforms, which form on low angle beaches, with strong onshore winds. Sand particles are moved from the beach, or the intertidal sandflat, further inland by wind (aeolian) activity, through the process of *saltation*. The sand particles are then stabilised as plants colonise the sand, allowing further deposition of sand to occur. Initially, on the upper beach, plants including prickly saltwort, sea rocket and common orache begin to stabilise sand movement, allowing salt tolerant plants, such as sand twitch and sand couch grass, to form small pioneer or embryo dunes. As marram grass colonises larger areas, its roots reduce sand movement, and the dunes become fixed, and higher. Eventually they may reach up to a height of 30 m.

The succession of plants on a sand dune forms a type of **prisere**, called a **psammosere**. The actual type of plant succession is dependent upon the calcium content, derived from shell fragments, of the sand. If it is high, as for example at Braunton Burrows (Devon) and Newborough Warren (Anglesey), a calcareous succession will develop.

STUDENT ACTIVITY 5.19

Refer to Figure 5.6.4 and identify the natural processes that are important in the formation of salt marshes.

FIGURE 5.6.4 The relationship between the abiotic and biotic components of a salt marsh ecosystem

If the dunes are mainly silica sand, a more acidic heath type of community develops (Figure 5.6.6). In the depressions or 'slacks' between the dunes, conditions are often wetter producing a **subclimax** plant community.

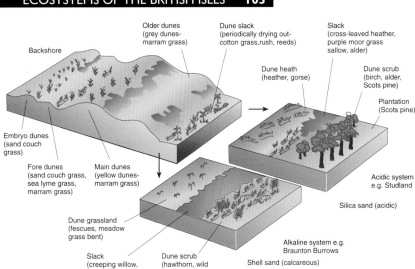

FIGURE 5.6.6 Acidic and alkaline sand dune successions

FIGURE 5.6.5 The distribution of the major sand dune systems in Britain

Dune systems, especially those dunes nearest to the sea, are very fragile. If the plant cover is disturbed either by natural erosion or human activity the strong onshore winds can produce a *'blow out'*, or deflation hollow, on the dune crest. Apart from their value in relation to wildlife and recreation, sand dunes are also important in terms of coastal protection against flooding.

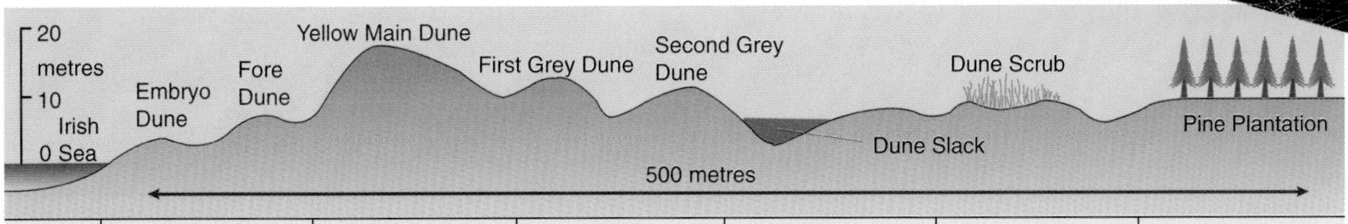

FIGURE 5.6.7 Sand dune habitats

	Mobile Embryo Fore dunes	Fixed Yellow dunes	Fixed Grey dunes	Dune slacks	Dune scrub	Pine plantation
Plant frequency %	Sand twitch 30 Sand couch grass 10 Sea lyme grass 10 Marram grass 70	Marram grass 60 Dune fescue 50 Sand sedge 20 Sea holly 5 Sea bindweed 5	Marram grass 10 Lichens 10 Mosses 20 Red fescue 20 Sand sedge 40 Sea holly 25 Sea bindweed 30	Round leaved wintergreen 10 Grass of Parnassus 4 Marsh helleborine 5 Marsh orchids 2	Heather 45 Gorse 10 Heath rush 10 Sea buckthorn 10 Creeping willow 5 Birch 5	Scot's pine 60 Dune helleborine orchid 1
Animal species	Oystercatchers Gulls	Skylark Ringed plover Sand lizard Sandhill snails	Skylark Ringed plover Sand lizard Sandhill snails Stonechat	Natterjack toad Warblers Dragonflies	Foxes Rabbits Small copper butterfly Kestrel	Red squirrel
pH	8.5	8.0	7.5	6.5	4.5	4.5
Soil	Unconsolidated sand with numerous shell fragments Very low organic content No water retention	Low organic content Little moisture retention	Brown humus layer several cms deep Some water retention	High organic content with peat forming Waterlogged gley soil	Black humus rich surface layer over an ash grey horizon over sand	Podsol Black humus rich surface layer over an ash grey horizon over an orange horizon

FIGURE 5.6.8 Plant community succession on the Ainsdale Dunes

CASE STUDY

The Ainsdale Sand Dunes National Nature Reserve

This reserve of 508 hectares is located on the Merseyside coast between Liverpool and Southport, and forms part of the impressive Sefton Coast dune system. Apart from its status as a National Nature Reserve, it is also a Ramsar Wetland of International Importance, and a candidate Special Area for Conservation (SAC) site. Details of the main habitats are given in Figure 5.6.8. The Ainsdale dunes are not on an estuary, but are the result of strong onshore winds from the Irish Sea moving sand inland.

The Reserve has over 400 species of flowering plants, and is therefore an important site for education and research. It is one of only a few sites where the rare natterjack toad occurs, and as part of the *Species Recovery Programme* new pools are being dug in the slacks to provide breeding sites. The Corsican pine woods are also being carefully managed to maintain a mixture of trees of different ages and types, as part of a similar Species Recovery Programme for red squirrels. In some areas, where it is felt that it is invading other habitats, scrub containing Corsican pine, birch, sea buckthorn and creeping willow is being removed in four phases. In the past the scrub had been partly controlled by the grazing of rabbits, but their numbers have been greatly reduced since the introduction of myxamotosis. Instead, during the winter months, Herdwick sheep from the Lake District are allowed to graze the Reserve. The removal of the water demanding scrub has allowed the height of the water table to increase. The Reserve is suffering from a decrease in the amount of sand moving along the coast from the south, probably due to hard engineering coastal defence structures, such as groynes, being built. This is having an effect both on the creation of embryo dunes, and on sand movement inland. If the system stabilises, scrub invasion will increase and the dune habitats will be lost. The problem requires a regional solution, and is being investigated by officers of the Sefton Coast Management Scheme.

STUDENT ACTIVITY 5.20

1 Analyse the changes in the plant communities and soils of the Ainsdale dunes shown on Figure 5.6.8.
2 How is this site being managed?

CASE STUDY

Ross Links, Northumberland

Since the 1950s, the Ross Links dune complex has been affected by several factors, perhaps the most important being:

■ the reduction in the effect of grazing by rabbits, due to the effects of myxamotosis on rabbit numbers,
■ an increase in the levels of grazing, from in the 1950s, 200 black faced sheep grazing all year, at a stocking rate of 0.6 per hectare together with 50 bullocks grazing during the winter to, in the 1980s, 300 sheep, at 1.3 per hectare and 400 cattle, and

■ various agricultural improvements, including fenced enclosures, local drainage, fertiliser application, dune flattening, planting shelterbelts, bracken eradication, and reseeding.

STUDENT ACTIVITY 5.21

Refer to 5.6.9 and explain how and why the vegetation communities of the Ross Links have changed since 1950.

FIGURE 5.6.9 Changes in habitat type at Ross Links, 1950–1986

Habitat type	Area 1950	Area %	Area 1964	Area %	Area 1986	Area %	Community type
Bare sand	22.2	6.8	6.1	1.8	2.1	0.7	Bare sand
Mobile dune	94.4	28.9	120.4	35.7	12.6	4.0	Marram grass
Fixed dune	71.7	21.9	107.3	31.8	100.2	31.6	Red fescue, Sand sedge
Dune heath	12.6	3.9	6.0	1.8	6.2	2.0	Ling heather
Agric. Improved	2.4	0.7	18.5	5.5	148.1	46.6	Common rye grass
Dune grassland	0.0	0.0	0.0	0.0	7.9	2.5	False oat grass
Dune slacks	69.8	21.3	35.2	10.4	37.0	11.7	Jointed rush
Bracken	54.0	16.5	44.2	13.1	3.5	1.1	Bracken

CASE STUDY

The Tees Estuary

The Tees Estuary is an internationally important site for resident and overwintering bird populations, including knot, cormorant, shelduck, redshank, sandwich tern, ringed plover, teal, purple sandpiper, bartailed godwit, grey plover, curlew, and turnstone. It also has a resident population of common seals, and is visited by grey seals and harbour porpoise.

The combination of available flat land and access to deep water has over the past 100 years seen large areas of the estuary developed for a variety of human activities which have included:

■ Land reclamation – In 1852 the area of intertidal mud and sandflats was 2254 hectares, today's figure is approximately 174 hectares.

■ Industry – Most of the land has been reclaimed for industries such as iron and steel, and chemicals, which require large sites. The major companies include Amoco, BASF, British Steel, Du Pont, ICI, Tioxide and Union Carbide.

■ Energy production – Teesside is connected by pipeline to the Ekofisk oil field in the North Sea and has several oil refineries. It is also the site of the Hartlepool nuclear power station and the Enron gas powered power station.

■ Port activities – The Tees and Hartlepool Port Authority Limited is among the top five ports in the UK in terms of tonnage handled, and can accommodate vessels up to a dry weight of 200 000 tonnes. Iron ore and coal are imported via the Redcar Ore Terminal, and oil and gas is exported from Phillips Petroleum. General cargo and containers are shipped through Tees Dock. These port activities require the frequent dredging of the main river channel.

■ Recreation – Tees Bay, especially, is used for a variety of activities, including sailing, cruising, windsurfing, and water skiing.

■ The Tees Barrage – At a cost of £50 m, the Tees Barrage was built between 1991 and 1994, to protect upstream areas against flooding, to improve navigation, to improve recreational facilities, and to allow fish to migrate along the river. It has in effect created a 22 km lake upstream from the barrage. The effects on the ecology, so far, appear to have been an increase in freshwater invertebrates, including riffle beetles and caddisfly, and a decrease in brackish water shrimps.

■ Waste disposal – The estuary receives domestic and industrial waste material from 44 sewage treatment works, and numerous industrial discharge points in the Tees catchment area.

■ Fishing – Prior to the 1930s, the estuary had an important fishing industry catching salmon, cockles, eels, flounder and whiting. Today, mainly due to the long term impact of pollution, commercial fishing is restricted to eels.

■ Coastal protection – As less than 10 per cent of the original intertidal area still exists, various measures have been taken to reduce erosion.

■ Coastal defence – Most of the Tees Estuary Management Plan area is below 5 metres above mean sea level, and coastal defence measures have been built to protect against a 50–100 year flood.

Not surprisingly water quality in the Tees estuary is a cause for concern. Figure 5.6.11 shows the degree of pollution in the estuary in 1970 and 1995. Conditions were very poor in the 1970s, especially if measured in terms of **Biological Oxygen Demand (BOD)**, which is the amount of oxygen required, normally measured over five days, to breakdown organic matter. In 1970, the BOD load was a very high 504 tonnes per day, especially between 5 and 25 km from the mouth of the estuary. By 1995 there had been an enormous improvement, with the BOD load dropping to 100 tonnes per day, but there are still problem areas near to the ICI Billingham outfall and Cargo Fleet sewage treatment works. High levels of nitrates and phosphates are contributing to the organic enrichment of parts of the estuary, especially Seal Sands. They have led to an increase in the growth, on the intertidal mudflats, of the green algae, *Enteromorpha* resulting in the deoxygenation of the mud, and a decline in the fauna, such as worms and mud snails. Concern has also been expressed about discharges of organic compounds such as PCBs (polychlorinated biphenyls) which are toxic to many organisms and which increase through the food chain by bioaccumulation. Many industries discharge heavy metals, such as cadmium, copper, and the dredging of the river channel, by disturbing the sediments, releases heavy metals which have accumulated over long periods, and which can also accumulate in various organisms. Oestrogenic chemical compounds, such as nonyl phenol, which mimic hormones and which have been seen to affect reproduction in fish, are produced on Teesside. Levels in the estuary are at 5 µg/l far below the minimum unsafe level of 20 µg/l.

A number of authorities are involved in the management of the estuary

■ *The Tees Local Environment Agency Plan*, dealing with pollution, fisheries, flood defence and conservation, has been prepared by the Environment Agency and covers the whole of the River Tees catchment area. A major aim is to improve the water quality of the estuary, and to restock it with salmon and trout.

■ *The Coastal Zone Management Strategy* covers the area between Crimdon Dene in the north and Staithes in the south. The Strategy has been prepared by the various local government authorities as an overall policy statement.

FIGURE 5.6.10 Tees Estuary Boat Yards

FIGURE 5.6.11 Changes in pollution levels on the River Tees between 1970 and 1995

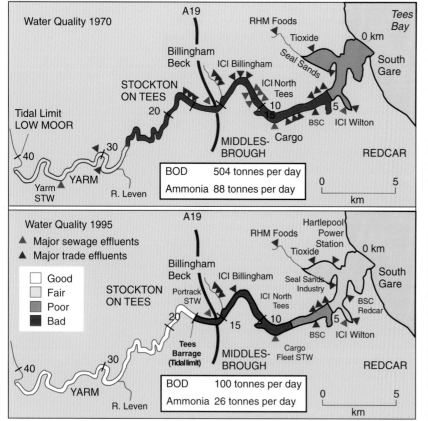

■ *The Shoreline Management Plan* sets out the strategy for coastal defence over the littoral sediment cell between Seaham Harbour in the north and Saltburn in the south. It has been prepared by the North Eastern Coastal Authorities Group, led by Hartlepool Borough Council. As over 90 per cent of the sediment, which has to be dredged from the estuary, is due to littoral drift, the dredged sediment is returned to the sea at a site 5 km off the coast. This allows it to re-enter the sediment cell, otherwise the coast would be subject to increased erosion rates, as is already occurring to the south of Redcar.

■ *The Tees Estuary Environment Scheme (TEES)* is a £200 m project by Northumbria Water and local industries, and is due to be completed by 2002. The scheme involves the transfer of existing partially treated sewage discharges from the sewage treatment works at Portrack, Eston and Cargo Fleet, together with industrial discharges from Wilton and Seal Sands, to a treatment plant at Bran Sands. It is planned to deal with 215 000 cu m of effluent per day.

■ *The Tees Estuary Management Plan* is a non-statutory document, produced through consultation with over 200 organisations, and seeks to inform, guide and advise on the current and future management of the estuary's environmental, social and economic resources.

■ The importance of large areas of the estuary for nature conservation is indicated by their designation, at three levels, as protected areas (Figure 5.6.12).

STUDENT ACTIVITY 5.22

1 Identify the major human activities affecting the Tees estuary.
2 Describe how the water quality of the Tees changed between 1970 and 1995.
3 Outline the main ways in which the Tees is being managed for nature conservation.
4 Recently it has been suggested that further industrial expansion should occur at Seal Sands. Assess the advantages and disadvantages of such a proposal.

FIGURE 5.6.12 Nature conservation and the Tees Estuary

International Designation managed by English Nature	National Designation managed by English Nature	Local Designation Managed by either Cleveland Wildlife Trust or a Local Authority
■ The Teesmouth and Cleveland Coast Special Protection Area (SPA) recognises the importance of the area for rare and migratory birds ■ The Seal Sands and Cowpen Marsh RAMSAR Site recognises the importance of the area for wetlands and waterfowl	SSSI: ■ Seaton Dunes and Common ■ South Gare and Coatham Sands ■ Seal Sands and North Gare Sands ■ Cowpen Marsh National Nature Reserve: ■ Teesmouth	Local Authority: Site of Nature Conservation Importance (SNCI) ■ 14 Sites Cleveland Wildlife Trust: ■ Portrack Marsh ■ Coatham Marsh

6

THE CONSERVATION AND MANAGEMENT OF ECOSYSTEMS

Key Ideas

■ Management of ecosystems represents people's attempts to effect change in plant and animal systems, which may be beneficial and constructive, rather than destructive to their environments.

■ For successful management it is necessary to fully understand the workings of ecosystems, the likely causes and effects of change, and the concept of sustainable yield.

■ Agricultural activity is particularly significant in creating major impacts on the functioning and structure of ecosystems, and on the appearance of landscapes through the impact of agro-chemicals, deforestation, drainage and intensification.

■ Policies decided at national and international level are having an increasingly significant impact on the conservation of wildlife, on agricultural systems, and on the people whose lives depend on such systems.

Earlier chapters have provided examples of the amazing variety of the earth's ecosystems. Many of them have been substantially altered by human activities, especially agriculture and forestry, and need to be managed to obtain a **sustainable yield**, where the resources obtained do not exceed the ecosystem's ability to replace them. The human activities, which attempt to alter them, should be beneficial and constructive, rather than destructive. Others, which are facing significant threats, or are unique, need to be protected or conserved. The successful management of an ecosystem can only be achieved through a full understanding of its structure, the interactions between its components, and the likely causes and effects of change.

6.1 Biodiversity

Group	Total of global species	Total of UK species	UK as a % of global total
Protozoa	40 000	20 000	50.0
Algae	40 000	20 000	50.0
Fungi	70 000	12 000	17.0
Ferns	12 000	80	0.7
Bryophytes	14 000	1000	7.0
Lichens	17 000	1500	9.0
Flowering plants	270 000	1400	0.5
Insects	1 000 000	22 500	2.0
Other invertebrates	300 000	6000	2.0
Freshwater fish	8500	40	0.5
Reptiles and amphibians	10 500	12	0.1
Mammals	4000	48	1.2
Birds	9500	210	2.0
Total	1 800 000	88 000	5.0

FIGURE 6.1.1 Species numbers in the UK and the World

The concept of **biodiversity** has received considerable attention following the 1992 United Nations Conference on Environment and Development (UNCED). Biodiversity may be simply defined as the variety of all types of living organisms, but UNCED defined it as 'the variability among living organisms from all sources including, *inter alia*, terrestrial, marine and other aquatic ecosystems and the ecological complexes of which they are part; this includes diversity within species, between species and of ecosystems'.

So far, approximately 1.8 m species of plants and animals have been identified (Figure 6.1.1). As there are still many parts of the world, particularly the tropical rainforests, where records are incomplete, estimates of the world's total number of species vary between 3 and 30 m.

The classification of organisms is called **taxonomy**, and traditionally living organisms are initially divided into four kingdoms, fungi, plant, animals, and prokaryotes (bacteria). Each kingdom is then subdivided into phylum, class, order, family, genus and species. The animal kingdom represents approximately 70 per cent of all species, with vertebrates (fish, reptiles, amphibians, mammals and birds) being represented by 41 000 species, and invertebrates (insects) by 1 300 000 species.

The world distribution of species shows a close correlation with latitude, with humid tropical areas such as the tropical rain forests having the largest number, and the polar regions having the lowest (Figure 6.1.2). The tropical rainforests and coral reefs have been described as biodiversity 'hot spots' because of the variety of species they contain. Of particular importance is their number of **endemic** species (those which are unique to a particular area). Brazil, the Democratic Republic of the Congo, Madagascar, and Indonesia have been identified by the WWF as 'megadiversity' countries because of the number of their endemic species.

The world's biodiversity of habitats and their species need to be conserved for a variety of reasons including the:

- maintenance of the earth's life systems,
- maintenance of the earth's genetic pool,
- potential future economic use of species as foods, or raw material sources,
- 'stewardship' of organisms, allowing them to be handed on to future generations, and an
- appreciation of the 'natural beauty' of plants and animals.

FIGURE 6.1.2 The relationship between the number of species of flowering plant and latitude. Each column represents a country spanning the latitude shown on the horizontal axis

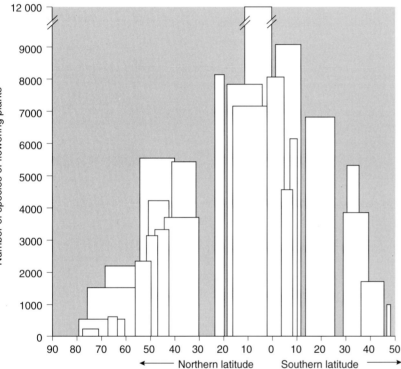

STUDENT ACTIVITY 6.1

1 Define the terms *sustainable yield, biodiversity, taxonomy* and *endemic*.
2 Explain the differences between the biodiversity of the UK and the World (Figure 6.1.1)

6.2 *Conservation and management*

Obviously, views on the environment and the need for landscape and nature conservation vary enormously. It is possible to see them as a continuum. At one extreme is the **ecocentric** view, which believes in the sustainable use of the earth's resources. In the middle is the neutral view, and at the other extreme is the **technocentric** or exploitative view (Figure 6.2.1).

The International Protection of Species and Habitats

Human activities, especially habitat destruction for agriculture and urbanisation, the introduction of non-endemic or alien species, and air, water and land pollution have caused a large number of plant and animal extinctions. The UK alone has lost 100 species since 1900, including 7 per cent of the country's dragonflies, 5 per cent of its butterflies, and 2 per cent of its fish and mammals.

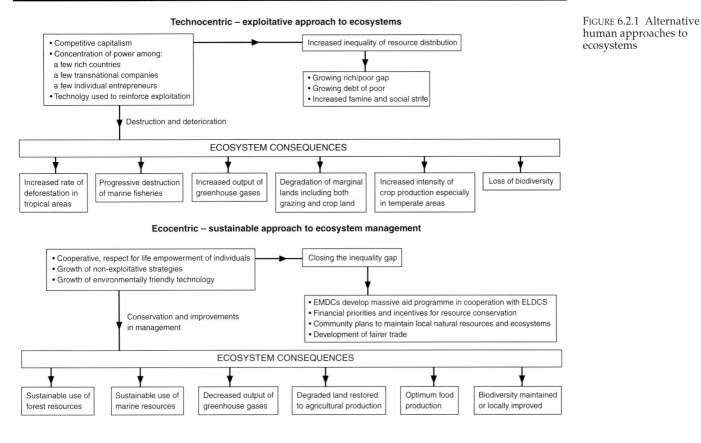

FIGURE 6.2.1 Alternative human approaches to ecosystems

STUDENT ACTIVITY 6.2

Compare the social, economic and environmental implications of the *technocentric* and *ecocentric* approaches to the environment.

International action to protect species and habitats has involved:

1 *International and national conservation legislation* – The framework for the conservation management of ecosystems is provided through international and national legislation, often based on the recommendations of international environmental conferences (Figure 6.2.2).

2 *The creation of protected habitats* – Several of the conventions have created internationally protected sites. Examples include Biosphere Reserves (1971 UNESCO Man and Biosphere Programme), Ramsar Sites (1971 Ramsar Convention on the Conservation of Wetlands), and World Heritage Sites (1972 World Heritage Convention).

3 *The establishment of a global monitoring system of endangered species* – The World Conservation Union (IUCN) produces lists, known as the Red Data Books, of endangered species. Species may be classified as being critically endangered, endangered or vulnerable. Examples of critically endangered animals include the black rhinoceros and the Crested ibis.

■ 1971 UNESCO Man and Biosphere Programme
■ 1971 Ramsar Convention on the Conservation of Wetlands of International Importance (especially as Waterfowl Habitat)
■ 1972 Convention Concerning the Protection of the World Cultural and Natural Heritage (the World Heritage Convention)
■ 1972 Oslo Convention for the Prevention of Marine Pollution by Dumping from Ships and Aircraft
■ 1973 Washington Convention on the International Trade in Endangered Species of Wild Fauna and Flora (CITES)
■ 1974 Paris Convention for the Prevention of Marine Pollution from Land Based Sources
■ 1979 Bonn Convention on the Conservation of Migratory Species of Wild Animals
■ 1979 Bern Convention on the Conservation of European Wildlife and Natural Habitats
■ 1985 International Whaling Commission commercial whaling moratorium
■ 1987 Montreal Protocol on the reduction of CFCs to protect the ozone layer
■ 1988 International Panel on Climate Change established
■ 1992 United Nations Conference on Environment and Development (UNCED) 'The Rio Earth Summit'
■ 1997 Kyoto Convention on the reduction of greenhouse gases

FIGURE 6.2.2 International conventions

The 1992 Rio de Janeiro United Nations Conference on Environment and Development (UNCED) 'The Rio Earth Summit' focused the attention of the world on the problems facing the environment. UNCED was attended by 157 countries, which were mainly represented by their heads of government, and it resulted in the production of five documents:

1   *The Rio Declaration on Environment and Development*
2   *Agenda 21* – A programme of action needed throughout the world to achieve a more sustainable pattern of development for the next century
3   *Convention on Biological Diversity* – An agreement about how best to protect the *diversity of habitats and species in the world*
4   *Framework Convention on Climatic Change* – An agreement for action to reduce the risks of global warming by limiting the emission of greenhouse gases
5   *Statement of Forest Principles* – An outline programme for the sustainable management and conservation of the world's forests.

STUDENT ACTIVITY 6.3

To what extent do you agree with groups such as the WWF and CITES that endangered species should be protected?

European Environmental Protection

In Europe, the member countries of the European Union (formerly the European Economic Community) have agreed a large number of environmental directives. The 'Birds' and Habitats' Directives have been particularly influential in nature conservation. The 1979 *'Birds Directive'* protects all wild birds and requires the countries of the EU to designate **Special Protection Areas** (SPAs) for rare and migratory bird species. The *'Habitats Directive'* lists 168 natural habitat types in Europe, which contain 632 plant and animal species requiring conservation. It is the main legislation for the implementation of the 1992 UNCED Biodiversity Convention within the EU. Member countries of the EU have to identify these habitats within their countries, and to designate them as **Special Areas of Conservation** (SACs). Britain contains 75 of the habitat types, including 22 priority habitat types including limestone pavements and Caledonian forest. The SPAs and SACs will form a network of protected sites throughout the EU, which will be known as *'Natura 2000'*. The 'Habitats Directive' has been implemented in Britain by the Conservation (Natural Habitats) Regulations 1994.

Some of the most important EU environmental directives are given in Figure 6.2.3.

FIGURE 6.2.3 EU Environmental Directives

- 1975 Surface Water Abstraction Directive (75/440/EEC)
- 1976 Bathing Waters Directive (76/217/EEC)
- 1976 Dangerous Substances Directive (76/464/EEC)
- 1978 Freshwater Fisheries Directive (78/659/EEC)
- 1979 Conservation of Wild Birds Directive (79/409/EEC) 'Birds Directive'
- 1982 Tioxide Directive (82/883/EEC)
- 1991 Urban Waste Water Treatment Directive (91/217/EEC)
- 1992 Conservation of Natural and Semi-natural Habitats and of Wild Flora and Fauna Directive (92/43/EEC) 'Habitats Directive'
- 1996 Integrated Pollution Prevention and Control Directive (96/61/EC)

6.3 Conservation and Management – Conservation in the UK

The considerable pressures on the countryside, and on particular habitats and species in the UK (Chapter 5), have led to the growth of both statutory environmental protection agencies and environmental pressure groups. A comprehensive programme of legislation has also been introduced with the aim of reducing the impact of these pressures.

Statutory environmental protection agencies

Figure 6.3.1 illustrates the UK's statutory environmental protection agencies, and their responsibilities.

The Joint Nature Conservation Committee (JNCC) coordinates the work of EN, SNH and the CCW. In England, in April 1999 the Countryside Commission merged with the Rural Development

	England	Wales	Scotland	Northern Ireland
Landscape Conservation	Countryside Agency	Countryside Council for Wales	Scottish Natural Heritage	
Nature Conservation	English Nature			Environment and Heritage Service
Environmental Protection		Environment Agency	Scottish Environmental Protection Agency	

FIGURE 6.3.1
Environmental agencies in the UK

Commission to form the *Countryside Agency*, introducing an integrated approach to the management of rural landscapes and rural community issues.

Environmental Pressure Groups

Environmental pressure groups are important for performing several functions. They may:

■ influence the government by political lobbying over environmental issues e.g. Friends of the Earth, and the Council for the Protection of Rural England,
■ directly intervene to stop activities which may damage habitats or wildlife e.g. Greenpeace,
■ purchase and manage their own nature reserves e.g. the Royal Society for the Protection of Birds, and the county Wildlife Trusts,
■ act as fund raisers to provide income for many environmental causes.

Environmental Legislation and protected areas in the UK

The legislation outlined in Figure 6.3.2 has created a comprehensive framework for the conservation of areas with important landscapes and wildlife in the UK:

1 *Landscape and Amenity conservation* – In England and Wales, areas with valuable 'attractive' landscapes have, in theory, been protected from unsuitable development by being designated, under the 1949 National Parks and Access to the Countryside Act, as either national parks or areas of outstanding natural beauty (AONB). Ten national parks, and the Broads Authority, have been designated (Figure 6.3.3). The purpose of the national parks was redefined by the 1995 Environment Act as being:

■ to conserve and enhance their natural beauty, wildlife and cultural heritage,
■ to promote opportunities for the understanding and enjoyment of the special qualities of the Parks by the public.

These two aims may at times conflict, and in those circumstances the 1995 Act states that greater weight should be attached to conservation. In Northern Ireland, AONBs are designated under the 1965 Amenity Lands Act, while in Scotland areas of valuable landscape are protected as National Scenic Areas (NSA).

2 *Nature conservation* – The most important habitats, and their plant and animal species, together with geological and geomorphological sites are protected as Sites of Special Scientific Interest (SSSI), or as National Nature Reserves (NNR) under the 1949 National Parks and Access to the Countryside, and the 1981 Wildlife and Countryside Acts. The 1949 Act also permits local authorities to designate Local Nature Reserves (LNR). In 1998, over 6300 SSSIs, and over 360 NNRs had been designated in the UK.

The 1995 Environment Act was very significant by:

■ redefining the National Parks as free-standing authorities with revised purposes and new duties,
■ creating the Environment Agency for England and Wales by incorporating the functions of Her Majesty's Inspectorate of Pollution, the National Rivers Authority and local Waste Regulation Authorities,
■ improving the regulations to protect important hedgerows,
■ introducing regulations to allow MAFF to operate the Countryside Stewardship Scheme,
■ requiring local authorities to carry out a review of old mineral planning permissions.

Date	Legislation	Date	Legislation
1938	Green Belt Act	1985	Food and Environment Protection Act
1947	Town and Country Planning Act	1985	Local Government Act
1949	National Parks and Access to the Countryside Act	1986	Agriculture Act
1968	Countryside Act	1990	Environmental Protection Act
1971	Town and Country Planning Act	1991	Water Resources Act
1974	Town and Country Planning Amenities Act	1991	Water Industry Act
1981	Wildlife and Countryside Act	1992	Sea Fisheries (Wildlife Conservation) Act
1981	Town and Country Planning (Minerals) Act	1992	Sea Fish (Conservation) Act
1982	Derelict Land Act	1995	Environment Act
1985	Wildlife and Countryside (Amendment) Act		

FIGURE 6.3.2
Conservation legislation

FIGURE 6.3.3 Protected areas in the UK

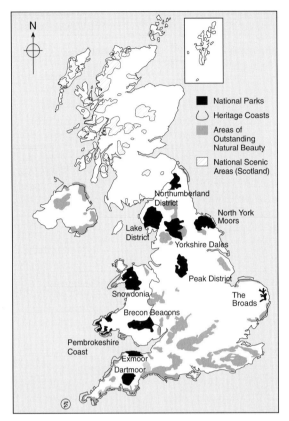

National Parks
Heritage Coasts
Areas of Outstanding Natural Beauty
National Scenic Areas (Scotland)

Northumberland District
North York Moors
Lake District
Yorkshire Dales
Peak District
Snowdonia
The Broads
Brecon Beacons
Pembrokeshire Coast
Exmoor
Dartmoor

FIGURE 6.3.4 Stickle Tarn, The Lake District National Park

Biodiversity and the UK

In response to the 1992 UNCED Conventions, in 1994, the UK government published:

Sustainable Forestry: The UK Programme
Climate Change: The UK Programme
Sustainable Development: The UK Strategy
Biodiversity: The UK Action Plan.

The aim of *Biodiversity: The UK Action Plan* is to conserve and enhance biological diversity within the UK, and to contribute to the conservation of global diversity through all appropriate mechanisms. It is a 20 year programme, which seeks to protect species through the identification of 38 key habitats for which Habitat Actions Plans are being prepared, together with 116 key Species Action Plans. An audit of UK biodiversity is being carried out, and important conservation sites are being designated as either Special Areas of Conservation (SACs) under the Habitats Directive or Special Protection Areas (SPAs) under the Birds Directive, as part of the EU Natura 2000 network of protected sites. In 1995, the second edition of *Biodiversity Challenge: an agenda for conservation in the UK*, a parallel report to *Biodiversity: The UK Action Plan*, was published by six UK conservation groups.

In England, the Countryside Commission has divided the country into 181 'Countryside Character Areas', and has produced Countryside Character descriptions, which suggest broad management policies for each area. English Nature has divided England into 97 land based, and 23 marine 'Natural Areas', which integrate with the 'Countryside Character Areas', and which can be used in broad scale nature conservation management.

STUDENT ACTIVITY 6.4

1 Summarise the ways in which landscape and wildlife are protected in the UK.
2 Explain why conservation groups would like to see the legislation strengthened.

FIGURE 6.3.5 Biodiversity Action Plans in the Yorkshire Dales National Park

Species Action Plans		Habitat Action Plans
Mammals	water vole, hare, otter, pipistrelle bat, red squirrel	upland mixed ash woodlands
Birds	skylark, song thrush, grey partridge	ancient hedgerows
Amphibian	great crested newt	upland hay meadow
Invertebrates	white-clawed crayfish	upland calcareous grassland
Plant	lady's slipper orchid	raised bog
		blanket bog
		upland heathland
		limestone pavement

Landscape and Habitat Changes in the UK

The landscapes and habitats of the UK are the product of the impact upon the environment of several thousands of years of human activities. In the last 50 years especially, the scale and intensity of the activities have increased significantly. The extent of the decline of a sample of habitats is illustrated in Figure 6.3.6. Even protected areas such as national parks and SSSIs are under threat. Damage to SSSIs may be either intentional, for example, by ploughing or deforestation, or unintentional through groundwater abstraction or fertiliser rich runoff from agricultural land. In 1998 it was reported that the Whernside SSSI, part of the Three Peaks in Yorkshire was in danger of losing its SSSI status due to overgrazing by sheep. Only 55 per cent of the English SSSIs were in a 'favourable' condition according to an English Nature report in 1997. New legislation is proposed for 1999 to strengthen the protection given to SSSIs.

Environmental Impact Assessment

In many countries, as part of the planning process, major land use developments are now subject to Environmental Impact Assessments (EIAs) to assess the effect they could have on sensitive landscapes and wildlife sites. Several methods may be used to carry out an EIA, one frequently used is the Leopold Matrix which links the existing environmental features to the proposed effects of a

Habitat type	Percentage loss
Neutral grassland (including hay meadows)	95
Grazing marsh	48
Calcareous grassland	80
Lowland heath	40
Fens and mires	50
Lowland bogs	60
Limestone pavements	43
Upland woodlands	28
Ancient woodlands	25

FIGURE 6.3.6 Habitat loss in England since 1930

development. Scores, for example from 1 = low to 10 = high, may be given to the scale or size of the impact, and the degree of damage it may cause. Total scores are obtained by adding the relevant rows or columns (Figure 6.3.7). An extension of this approach is to view landscape and wildlife as critical natural or environmental capital, and attempt to place a financial value on them.

FIGURE 6.3.7 An outline Leopold Matrix

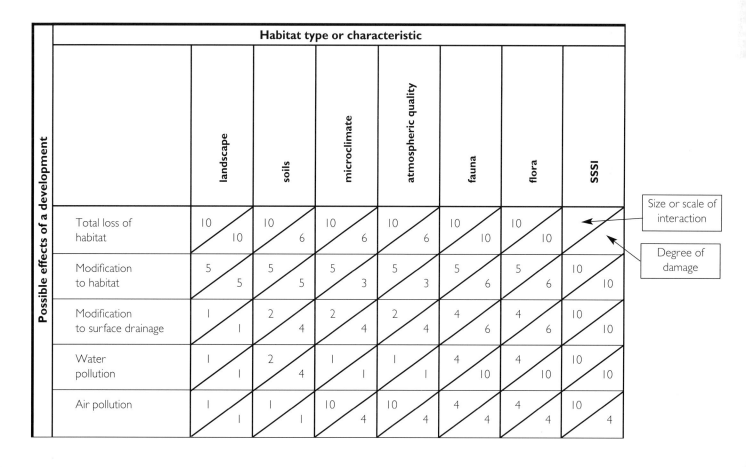

FIGURE 6.3.8 Land use changes 1970s–1980s in all eleven national parks

Land Use	Change sq. km	Land Use	Change sq. km
cultivated land	74.9	water and wetland	6.8
improved pasture	66	developed land	10.8
bracken	−19.2	scrub	−5.2
grass moor	−49.1	rock and coastal	15.2
upland heath	−30.9	Field Boundaries	Change kms
coniferous forest	178.5	hedgerows	−1212.7
broadleaf woodland	9.2	fences	346.7
rough pasture	−133	walls	−411.6

STUDENT ACTIVITY 6.6

Refer to Figure 6.3.8, and describe and suggest reasons to explain the land use changes in the national parks.

Urban development and habitat loss

The growth of urban areas and their related transport networks are obviously an example of a very intensive type of development, which is a major cause of both changes to the landscape and habitat loss. Through the 1938 Green Belt Act, and the 1947 Town and Country Planning Act, together with subsequent amendments, the various local authorities are, in theory, able to control the pressures caused by urban growth. In 1997 the government announced the need by 2016 for an additional 4.4 m homes. Figure 6.3.9 illustrates the projected regional distribution. Initially the government proposed that 60 per cent of the new homes should be built on 'greenfield' sites, but after public opposition it was recommended that 40 per cent should be 'greenfield', with the remainder on urban 'brownfield' sites.

FIGURE 6.3.9 Projected rural land loss to 2016

Region	Rural land lost sq. km
Home Counties and South East	495
South West	308
East Midlands	212
West Midlands	158
Yorkshire and Humberside	155
East Anglia	148
North West	135
North	93

STUDENT ACTIVITY 6.7

1 On an outline map of England, showing the economic regions, plot the data in Figure 6.3.9.
2 Explain the reasons for this projected distribution of new housing development.
3 What are the environmental consequences?

Agri-environment conservation

The activity which has had the largest impact in terms of the land area affected is agriculture. In the 1930s fourteen per cent of the British workforce were employed in agriculture, today the figure is only 1.4 per cent, yet output has dramatically increased. Wheat yields, for example, have increased from 2.1 tonnes per hectare in 1925 to 7.7 in 1995. The increasing use of machines, agrochemicals, and modern management techniques are obviously the reason. The increases in output have, unfortunately, had a major effect on the landscape and wildlife of the country. Since 1945, 40 per cent of the UK's hedgerows have been destroyed, and 97 per cent of its hay meadows have been lost.

Although the changes started during World War II, the degree of change increased after the UK joined the EEC in 1973, and implemented the Common Agricultural Policy (CAP). Farmers were encouraged to maximise productivity by being paid a guaranteed price for their products. The CAP provided incentives for increasing output, which in many areas led to the intensification of agriculture often involving:

■ the creation of larger fields, by the removal of hedgerows and other field boundaries, to allow larger machinery to be used,
■ pollution of both drinking water and rivers and lakes, through the effect of agro-chemicals (fertilisers, pesticides, and insecticides),
■ the drainage of lowland grazing marshes and upland moorland,
■ the widespread use, on livestock, of antibiotics (leading to the development of resistant bacteria) and, until they were banned by the EU, of growth hormones,
■ the increasing threat from biotechnology and genetically modified (GM) crops.

Organic farming, where agro-chemicals are not used, and where livestock are reared using less intensive methods, is expanding rapidly but, unfortunately, in many areas is unable to meet the demand from customers, particularly the major supermarkets.

Increasing concern over the effects of the intensification of farming led in 1987, through the 1986 Agriculture Act, to the creation of Environmentally Sensitive Areas (ESAs).

Farmers in each ESA are eligible for a range of grants from MAFF, in return for following environmentally friendly approaches to agriculture (Chapter 5). By 1998 there were 43 ESAs in the UK (Figure 6.3.10). As well as creating ESAs the 1986 Agriculture Act introduced various measures known as ALURE, 'alternative land uses in rural economy'. The incentive behind this scheme were the changes to the EU Common Agricultural Policy (CAP), which sought to reduce agricultural food surpluses by taking agricultural land out of production. In the case of the UK it was estimated that 2 m hectares would have to be taken out of production. One alternative was Set Aside, where farmers were given grants for taking a minimum of 20 per cent of their land out of production. The 1987 Department of Environment Circular 'Development Involving Agricultural Land' relaxed the planning controls over agricultural land and suggested the development of non-agricultural uses such as golf courses. Additionally, the Farm Woodland Scheme, which came into existence in 1988, funded by MAFF and the Forestry Commission, provided grants to farmers for planting trees on land, which had previously been used for agriculture. The Farm Conservation Grant Scheme (FCGS) was initiated in 1989 by MAFF to provide grants to farmers for a range of schemes including bracken control, improving hedges, protecting natural woodland and regenerating heather. The Farming and Rural Conservation Agency (FRCA) is a new agency established by MAFF to implement policies on farming and conservation. Following growing concern over the effect of nitrates on freshwater ecosystems, and public water supplies, in 1990 a pilot scheme was initiated to reduce nitrate levels in the runoff from agricultural land. In England, ten Nitrate Sensitive Areas (NSAs) were established, together with nine Nitrate Advisory Areas (NAAs). As with the ESAs, farmers in the NSAs were eligible for grants. In 1992, the CAP was reformed with quotas being introduced, and subsidies linked to the area farmed rather than the quantity of food produced.

In 1991, the Countryside Commission launched the Countryside Stewardship Scheme, which by providing grants to farmers for environmental improvement schemes aimed to help to reverse the declining quality of some of the most valued English landscapes, countryside features, and the wildlife habitats that they support. In 1994 it also incorporated the Hedgerow Incentive Scheme. By 1995 it involved 4937 agreements covering 91 403 hectares. Following the 1995 Environment Act the administration of the Scheme became the responsibility of MAFF.

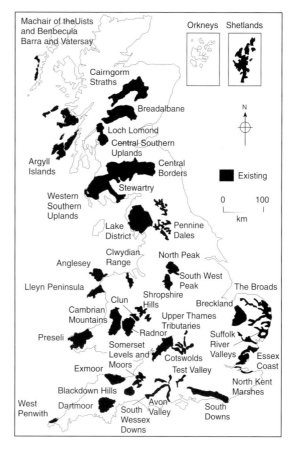

FIGURE 6.3.10
Environmentally Sensitive Areas (ESAs) in Britain

English Nature also provides grants for habitat improvement on SSSIs owned or managed by farmers, through either the Reserve Enhancement Scheme or the Wildlife Enhancement Scheme.

STUDENT ACTIVITY 6.8

Outline the advantages and disadvantages of the changes in the methods of farming in the UK since 1945.

FIGURE 6.3.11

Countryside groups fear for tree sparrow's future

Britain's humblest songbird is facing devastation from agro-chemicals, along with other once common birds, according to a new report commissioned by six countryside groups including the Royal Society for the Protection of Birds. Numbers of the small bird have collapsed by 89 per cent between 1969 and 1994. The grey partridge is down by 82 per cent and the skylark by 59 per cent.

Ornithologists contributing to the document blame the use of insecticides and weedkiller sprays for destroying the food chain on which the birds depend.

Insecticide dosing of farmland rose from 5 per cent of crop in 1970 to 90 per cent in 1990. In the same period, herbicide use rose from an average 1.3 sprayings of a field annually to 2.5. The decline is also blamed on the loss of hedges – ideal for shelter and nesting, and a shift from spring to autumn ploughing which leaves less cover in winter.

Guardian 7 February 1997

The CAP is due to be reformed again through the Agenda 2000 proposals. In the UK in 1998, £3.5 bn was paid to farmers as subsidies, and £6.5 bn was used to protect market prices. The total CAP payments of £10 bn is equivalent to £180 per person per year.

Conservation management of specific sites

Many habitats are also popular recreational destinations, and the combination of habitat fragility and visitor pressure may produce a conflict of aims which requires careful management. Visitor management will require the provision of visitor access areas requiring the careful location of car parks, clearly signed footpaths, picnic areas, litter bins, and the creation of nature trails and information boards. Habitat management aims to maintain or improve the diversity of habitats and species on the site. This may involve controlling the invasion of unwanted plant species, or creating new habitats. Routine maintenance, through estate management, of site features such as paths and fences, is also required.

CASE STUDY

The North York Moors National Park

FIGURE 6.3.12 Land use types of the NYMNP

Land use type	Area in sq. km	Percentage	Changes 1970s to 80s sq. km
cultivated land	320.9	22.3	8.2
improved pasture	266.4	18.6	−0.8
bracken	123.3	8.9	−2.9
grass moor	9	0.6	−0.2
upland heath	355.7	24.8	3.2
coniferous forest	213.7	14.9	3.2
broadleaf woodland	99.9	7.0	2.6
rough pasture	22.4	1.6	−2.2
developed land	18.7	1.3	0.6
Total	1436	100	

FIGURE 6.3.14 North York Moors National Park – Moorland loss since 1950

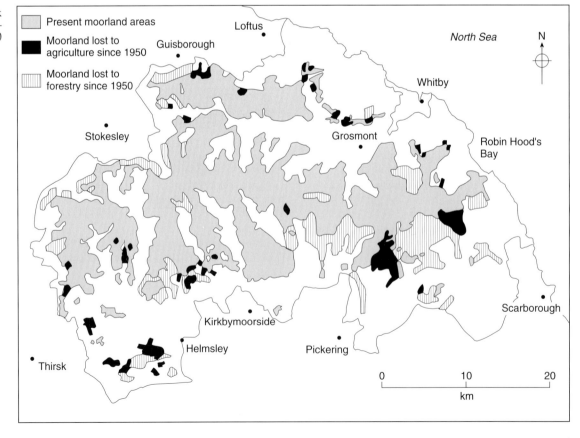

Designated in 1952, the North York Moors National Park (NYMNP) was the sixth national park to be created in England and Wales. It has a variety of landscapes and habitats (Figure 6.3.12 and 6.3.13), but is probably best known for its extensive area of heath moorland. Following the 1995 Environment Act, in common with the other English national parks, the NYMNP became on the 1 April 1997 a unitary National Park Authority (NPA) with additional responsibilities. The NPA is required to produced a National Park Management Plan (NPMP) within three years of being established, and in June 1997 the Moors NPA issued a draft NPMP for public consultation.

FIGURE 6.3.13 Moorland habitat types

Moorland habitats	Area sq. km	Percentage
Dry heath	274.4	55
Wet heath	94.8	19
Bracken	79.8	16
Mires	25.0	5
Acid grassland	15.0	3
Other	10.0	2

The management of the ecosystems of the NYMNP

A large number of management schemes, financed by the Park Authority itself, MAFF, English Nature or the EU, are involved in reducing the potential conflict between the conservation, economic, social and recreational uses of the Park, and in improving its environment.

Statutory protection

The most important wildlife sites are protected by SSSI and/or National Nature Reserve status. Within the Park, 58 areas have been designated as SSSIs, covering 6006 hectares, or 4.2 per cent of the Park. Two areas, Forge Valley Woods and Duncombe Park are NNRs, and Farndale is a Local Nature Reserve. As in the other national parks, nature conservation has to be with the agreement of the landowners as the majority of land is privately owned. The heath moorland habitat of the Park is a potential Special Protection Area (SPA) for golden plover and merlin.

1 *The upland moorland* – Since 1853, when records first began, over 200 sq km of the heather moorland of the Park have been lost. The major reasons include:

■ *Agricultural reclamation*, which has been concentrated on the more productive soils, found on the Corallian limestone of the Tabular Hills in the south of the Park, a good example being Lockton Low Moor.
■ *Afforestation* – Most of the loss to forestry has occurred in the eastern part of the Park, as the Forestry Commission has created large coniferous plantations such as Dalby Forest.
■ *Recreational Pressure* – A survey of the Cleveland Way in 1988 revealed that 23 per cent of its length was severely eroded, especially the section on the Cleveland Hills where its route coincided with that of the Lyke Wake Walk (Figure 6.3.15).

■ *Military use* – Large areas of Fylingdales Moor form the site of RAF Fylingdales, part of the international early warning radar system. In 1994 the three famous 'golf balls' housing the radar were replaced by a radar pyramid.
■ *Fire* – In the hot, dry summer of 1976, the moorlands were affected by 85 fires, four of which were particularly large. On Glaisdale Moor, 500 hectares, were burnt by fires with temperatures up to 700°C. The fires started in early June, and despite heavy rainfall in September did not go out until February 1977.
■ *Bracken encroachment* – Bracken is a particular problem on the moorlands. In 1988 it covered 28 per cent (225 sq km) of the Park, occurring particularly on the upper valley slopes and the edge of the moorland plateau. Bracken is highly invasive being able to spread both by spores and by underground rhizomes. It suppresses other plants, is mildly poisonous to sheep and highly poisonous to cattle. The major problem, however, is that it provides a habitat for ticks, which have caused high death rates of both lambs and grouse chicks, and can produce Lyme disease in humans.
    In 1976 the Park Authority established the *Moorland Management Scheme* to provide advice and grant aid. The Scheme includes:
■ *The Integrated Bracken Control Programme* – The aim being to reduce, by aerial spraying with the herbicide Asulox, the area of moorland covered by bracken.
■ *The Moorland Regeneration Programme* – In 1995 the Park Authority announced this four year programme, which is costing £2 m and is financed by MAFF, the NPA, and the European Union Northern Uplands Objective 5b Programme. The aim of the Programme is to reduce the high levels of lamb and grouse chick mortality, caused by the effects of sheep tick and bracken.
■ *Moorland Restoration Programme* – This commenced, in 1984, on Glaisdale Moor with the area burnt in 1976 being fenced, and various restoration techniques tried, including reseeding with heather brash (a mixture of heather cuttings

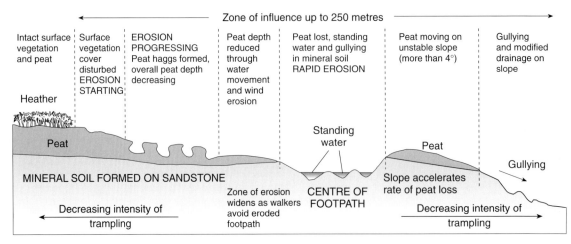

FIGURE 6.3.15 The effects of trampling on the Lyke Wake Walk

Zone of influence up to 250 metres

Intact surface vegetation and peat

Surface vegetation cover disturbed EROSION STARTING

EROSION PROGRESSING Peat haggs formed, overall peat depth decreasing

Peat depth reduced through water movement and wind erosion

Peat lost, standing water and gullying in mineral soil RAPID EROSION

Peat moving on unstable slope (more than 4°)

Gullying and modified drainage on slope

Heather

Peat

MINERAL SOIL FORMED ON SANDSTONE

Standing water

Peat

Gullying

Decreasing intensity of trampling

Zone of erosion widens as walkers avoid eroded footpath

CENTRE OF FOOTPATH

Slope accelerates rate of peat loss

Decreasing intensity of trampling

containing seeds). The site is being carefully monitored to assess the effectiveness of the various techniques in regenerating the heath community. A similar scheme is being implemented on Fylingdales Moor.

■ *The Cleveland Way Project* – This Project was established, in 1988, with a management strategy being produced in 1989. A major programme of footpath restoration began in 1992. Restoration techniques have included using sandstone slabs on the flatter sections, angled stones on the steeper slopes, improved drainage, regrading the slope angle, and reseeding bare ground. Restoration work has already been completed on Cringle Moor, Cold Moor, and Roseberry Topping.

■ *Land purchase by the Park Authority* – Between 1976 and 1985, concerned at the rate of loss of moorland to agriculture, the Park Authority bought 1356 hectares of the Levisham Estate, Nab Farm and Lockton High Moor.

2 *Woodland* – Only 5 per cent, 7200 hectares, of the Park is covered by semi-natural broadleaf woodland, with most of the areas being confined to the steeper valley sides. Under the *Woodland Grant Scheme* grants are available from the Forestry Authority, for landowners to expand the size of their woodlands. *Yorwoods* is a farm woodland initiative using EU Objective 5b and MAFF funds. Coniferous forests, mainly plantations, cover 17 per cent or 25 650 hectares, most of which is owned by the Forestry Commission, of the Park. Their large plantations, which make up the North Riding Forest Park produce 80 000 tonnes of timber a year, and are visited for recreational purposes by 1.5 m people a year.

3 *Rivers* – The NYMNP is mainly drained by the River Derwent and the River Esk. The River Esk is Yorkshire's only salmon and sea trout river, and is also important for otters, bank voles, kingfishers and freshwater pearl mussels. *The River Esk Regeneration Programme* is a £290 000 scheme funded by the EU, MAFF and the NPA, which aims to improve the water quality for fish and other wildlife. The Environment Agency has also produced *Local Environment Agency Plans (LEAP)* for both the Derwent and the Esk.

4 *Coast* – The entire coast is part of the *Heritage Coast Management Plan*. Staithes, Runswick Bay, Sandsend and Robin Hood's Bay are all designated under the EU Directive on the quality of bathing waters, and Yorkshire Water has introduced the 'Coastcare' scheme to improve sewage treatment.

5 *Agro-ecosystems* – Agriculture, with a total workforce of 2843, is the second largest employer in the Park. There are 705 full time and 620 part time holdings. Much of the heather moorland is managed for sheep grazing and grouse rearing, and concern has been expressed over stocking levels, and the illegal killing of birds of prey, including hen harriers. The most intensive type of farming occurs around the edges of the central moorland, particularly in the south on the more fertile soils of the Tabular Hills.

Various agri-environment schemes provide grants for environmental conservation management projects on farms:

■ *The Countryside Stewardship Scheme* is implemented by MAFF, and tends to cover those areas of the Park not covered by other schemes. In 1996 it involved 71 farms covering an area of 1345 hectares.

■ *The North York Moors Farm Scheme, Upland Management Scheme*, and *Alternate Land Use (ALU) Programme* are all Park Authority Schemes.

STUDENT ACTIVITY 6.9

Imagine that you are on work experience with the NYM National Park Authority and have been asked to produce a 5 year management plan for the Park:
1 Identify the main habitats of the Park, and summarise recent changes in their extent.
2 Produce a table summarising the major issues facing the Park, and possible solutions.
3 Prepare an information leaflet for walkers, to explain the causes and effects of footpath erosion, and provide guidance on how they can help to minimise the problem.

Glossary

abiotic non-living material

abstraction the removal of water from a river (surface water abstraction) or from groundwater for domestic, industrial or agricultural use

aeolian erosion the erosion of sediment by the wind

ahermatypic coral those which are solitary

anthropogenic the effect of human activities

autotroph producer organisms such as plants and phytoplankton which convert insolation into living material

biodiversity the variety of species in an ecosystem

biological oxygen demand (BOD) a measure of the amount of oxygen required to breakdown a pollutant (the amount of oxygen used in five days for the partial oxidation of a sample of effluent)

biomass the total amount of living material found in a given area

biome an ecosystem which extends over a large area, with similar soil and climatic conditions

biosphere the zone of the Earth containing living organisms

biotechnology the use of advances in biological technology to produce high yielding varieties (HYV) of plants, and animals with specific qualities, its most recent application is in genetically modified (GM) plants and animals

biotic living organisms

brown forest earth the soil type associated with deciduous woodland in cool temperate areas

brown Mediterranean the soil type associated with woodland in warm temperate (Mediterranean) areas

calcicoles plants which prefer calcareous (alkaline) habitats

calcifuges plants which prefer acidic (non-calcareous) habitats

carnivores animals or plants which eat animals

chernozem a soil type associated with temperate interior grasslands

cinnamon a transitional soil type found between Mediterranean and desert soils

climax community a 'stable' community, which is in balance with the prevailing abiotic conditions, at the end of a succession

common agricultural policy (CAP) the agricultural policy applied to all the member nations of the European Union which establishes market prices, quotas, subsidies, etc.

community the population of plants and animals in a specific habitat

convergent evolution a process where similar habitat conditions in separate areas evolve similar organisms

decomposers organisms which break down organic matter, releasing nutrients

desertification a process of land degradation occurring in semi-arid areas

detrivores organisms which feed on partly decomposed material

dipterocarps types of tree, including some of the largest in the World, which mainly occur in the tropical rainforests of southeast Asia

ecocentric an environmental point of view which stresses the importance of the maintenance of the Earth's natural physical systems

ecological niche an organism's specific role in an ecosystem

ecology the science which investigates the relationships of living organisms to each other, and their environment

ecotone a transitional zone between two ecosystems

eluviated a soil horizon formed by the removal of material such as clay

endemic an organism which is only found in a specific location

environmental impact assessment (EIA) a method of assessing the impact of human activities on landscapes and wildlife

environmentally sensitive areas (ESA) areas which receive grants to allow them to be farmed in a way which maintains or improves the environment

epiphytes plants which grow on the surface of other plants

eutrophication an increase in an aquatic ecosystem's nutrient levels, particularly following the addition of nitrates and phosphates as a consequence of human activities

ferrallitic the soil type associated with tropical rainforests

ferruginous a soil type associated with tropical savanna grasslands

food chain a sequence of organisms linked by a flow of energy in the form of food

food web a complex of inter-linked food chains

gley a waterlogged soil horizon

gully erosion a type of erosion where surface flow is channelled producing deep gullies

habitat the location which forms the normal environment for a particular organism

halosere a plant succession commencing in salt water

herbivore a plant eating animal

hermatypic coral those that are colonial, forming reefs

heterotroph consuming organisms, which may be herbivores, carnivores or omnivores

horizon a section of a soil profile with specific characteristics

humus decomposed organic material which is incorporated into the A horizon of a soil

hydrosere a plant succession commencing in fresh water

illuviated a soil horizon into which material including clay, bases, and sesquioxides is deposited from the eluviated horizon

Inter-Tropical Convergence Zone a low pressure area formed where two air masses meet producing cloud, and rain

laterite a weathered deposit, consisting of hydrated iron and aluminium oxides found in tropical soils, which on exposure at the surface may form a very hard layer

lianes climbing plants in the tropical rainforest

minerotrophic peat areas, such as fens, receiving water and nutrients from groundwater or springs

mycorrhizal organisms including fungi, associated with plant rootlets, which decompose material releasing nutrients

net primary productivity the rate of accumulation of living material in a given area over a certain period

ombrotrophic peat areas, such as raised bogs, receiving water and nutrients from rainwater

omnivores organisms which eat both plants and animals

palaeoecology the study of the ecology of ancient geological environments

palynology the study of fossil pollen to identify plant successions

phosphate stripping the removal of phosphates from sewage effluent at sewage treatment works, nitrate stripping is a similar process

phototrophs organisms which are able to photosynthesise

phytoplankton microscopic organisms in both fresh and sea water that can carry out photosynthesis

plagioclimax a 'stable' community formed as a result of human activities

podsol the soil type associated with coniferous forest and heath

prisere an original plant succession consisting of several stages, called seres, developed from a bare surface

psammosere a plant succession on sand dunes

Ramsar site wetland habitats protected by the Convention on Wetlands of International Importance Especially as Waterfowl Habitat (the Ramsar Convention) 1973

red Mediterranean (terra rossa) the soil type which normally occurs in the eroded remains of brown Mediterranean soils developed on limestone

red tides 'blooms' of algae associated with eutrophication

regolith the inorganic weathered layer of a surface parent rock

respiration the breakdown of organic compounds, involving the release of energy

Sahel the area in West Africa between the Sahara Desert and the savanna

saprophytes plants and fungi which obtain nutrients from dead and decaying organisms

sclerophyllous plants with hard, waxy leaves, which occur in Mediterranean areas

sere a plant community developed at a stage in a prisere

sheet wash a thin film of surface runoff which erodes the top layer of sediment

sierozems a soil associated with desert areas

Sites of Special Scientific Interest (SSSI) wildlife areas of high quality which are protected by law

soil catena a sequence of soils developed along a slope

Special Area of Conservation (SAC) habitats or species protected by the EU habitats directive (92/43/EEC)

Special Protection Area (SPA) habitats particularly important for birds protected by the EU birds directive (79/409/EEC)

stratum specificity the adaptation of an organism to live in a particular niche in a specific layer of an ecosystem, for example, the tree canopy

subclimax a plant community formed when a natural factor prevents a succession from reaching its climax community

subsere a plant succession which forms when the arresting factors which formed a plagioclimax or a subclimax community are no longer present allowing the succession to develop towards a 'normal' climax community

sustainable yield the organic yield of an ecosystem which can be obtained without exceeding its capacity to replace it

taxonomy a system of biological classification

technocentric a point of view which maintains that humans have the ability to dominate the environment by using technology to overcome problems or to extract resources

xerophytes plants which can tolerate dry conditions

zooplankton microscopic animals which feed on phytoplankton

zooxanthellae a type of photosynthetic algae which grows in a symbiotic relationship with coral polyps

General References

Briggs D and Smithson P, 1985, *Fundamentals of Physical Geography*, Hutchinson
Digby B (Ed.), 1995, *The Physical Environment*, Heinemann
Goudie A, 1984, *The Nature of the Environment*, Blackwell
Goudie A, 1986, *The Human Impact on the Natural Environment*, Blackwell
Goudie A (Ed.), 1997, *The Human Impact Reader*, Blackwell
Goudie A and Viles H, 1997, *The Earth Transformed*, Blackwell
Law N and Smith D, 1987, *Decision Making Geography*, Hutchinson
Mottershead R, 1979, *Biogeography*, Blackwell
Naish M and Warn S (Eds.), 1997, *16–19 Core Geography*, Longman
Owen L and Unwin T (Eds.), 1997, *Environmental Management*, Blackwell
Pears N, 1977, *Basic Biogeography*, Longman
Prosser R, 1995, *Managing Environmental Systems*, Nelson
Sarre P (Ed.), 1991, *Environment, Population and Development*, Hodder and Stoughton
Silvertown J and Sarre P (Eds.), 1990, *Environment and Society*, Hodder and Stoughton
Simmons I G, 1974, *The Ecology of Natural Resources*, Arnold
Simmons I G, 1979, *Biogeography: Natural and Cultural*, Arnold
Simmons I G, 1982, *Biogeographical Processes*, George Allen and Unwin
Smith P and Warr K (Eds.), 1991, *Global Environmental Issues*, Hodder and Stoughton
Waugh D, 1995, *Geography: An Integrated Approach*, Nelson
Woodfield J (Ed.), 1994, *Ecosystems and Human Activity*, Collins Educational

Chapter 1

Bridges E M, 1970, *World Soils*, Cambridge
Courtney F M and Trudgill S T, 1976, *The Soil*, Arnold
Curtis L F, Courtney F M and Trudgill S, 1976, *Soils in the British Isles*, Longman

Chapter 2

Foskett R and Foskett N, 1993, Community news: site for a new plant, *Geog. Review* **7** (2) pp 7–9
Soper R, 1994, *Biological Science 1*, Cambridge
Williams G, 1987, *Techniques and Fieldwork in Ecology*, Collins

Chapter 3

Cleary M, 1994, Timber and tribes: logging the forests of Borneo, *Geog. Review* **8** (1) pp 38–41
Farbrother D, Tilling S, Holmes D and Sanders R, 1996, Tropical forests in Malaysia, *Geog. Review* **10** (1) pp 20–27

Field Studies Council, 1997, *Tropical forests and human impact*
Higgitt D, 1998, The rainforest paradox, *Geog. Review* **12** (1) pp 7–9
Park C, 1988, Acid rain: trans-frontier air pollution, *Geog. Review* **2** (1) pp 20–24
Trudgill S, 1990, The sustainable use of forests, *Geog. Review* **4** (1) pp 11–13
Whyatt D and Metcalfe S, 1995, Sulphur emissions and acid rain, *Geog. Review* **9** (1) pp 14–18

Chapter 4

Brown T and Mugglestone F, 1994, *The Aral Sea*, Longman
Brydges T and Wilson R, 1991, Acid rain since 1985 – times are changing, in Owen L and Unwin T (Eds.), 1997, *Environmental Management*, Blackwell
Goudie A, 1992, Global warming and the arid lands, *Geog. Review* **6** (1) pp 37–41
Middleton N, 1993, The desertification debate, *Geog. Review* **7** (1) pp 30–33
Ormond R and Douglas A (Eds.), 1996, The exploitation of coral reefs, *Ecological issue* no. 7, British Ecological Society

Chapter 5

Angel H, 1981, *The Natural History of Britain and Ireland*, Rainbird
Black K, 1998, Saltmarshes and succession, *Geog. Review* **12** (1) pp 25–27
Boardman J, 1992, Agriculture and Erosion in Britain, *Geog. Review* **6** (1) pp 15–19
Chaffey J, 1994, *A New View of Britain*, Hodder and Stoughton
Chaffey J, 1997, *Managing Environments in Britain and Ireland*, Hodder and Stoughton
Drewitt A, 1991, *The Vegetation of the Yorkshire Dales National Park*, Yorkshire Dales National Park Committee
Environment Agency, 1996, *Tees Local Environment Agency Plan*, Environment Agency
Lacey J, 1997, *Tees Estuary Management Plan*, INCA
McTernan M, 1993, The Heather Moorland Ecosystem, *Geog. Review* **7** (2) pp 2–6
Morris P (Ed.), 1979, *Natural History of the British Isles*, Hamlyn
Robinson D and Blackman J, 1990, Water erosion of arable land on the South Downs, *Geog. Review* **4** (1) pp 19–23

Chapter 6

British Ecological Society, 1996, Actions for Biodiversity in the UK, *Ecological issue* **6**
Countryside Commission, 1991, *Landscape Change in the National Parks*
North Yorks Moors National Park Authority, 1997, *North York Moors National Park Management Plan Consultation Draft*

Index